DECORATIVE PLASTERWORK
REPAIR AND
RESTORATION

Cheltenham   Gloucestershire

Restored Regency external plastering

DECORATIVE PLASTERWORK REPAIR AND RESTORATION

W D Stagg and R Masters

ATTIC
BOOKS

First published in 1983 by Orion Books
Second edition published in 1986 by
Attic Books, The Folly, Rhosgoch, Painscastle, Builth Wells, Powis LD2 3JV

British Library Cataloguing in Publication Data

Stagg, W. D.
 Decorative plasterwork: its repair and
 restoration.—2nd ed.
 1. Plasterwork, Decorative—Conservation
 and restoration
 I. Title II. Masters, Ronald
 693'.6 NA3690

ISBN 0 948083 06 9

Printed in Great Britain by J W Arrowsmith Ltd, Bristol

Contents

Authors' preface   vi

1 Introduction to antique plasterwork   1
   Materials and methods   1
   Fibrous plasterwork   3

2 Internal plain surfacing   7
   Texture   12

3 Preparatory work   13
   General principles   13
   Running moulds   19
   Forming elliptical curves   19
   Squeezes   21
   Removal of ceilings for renovation   22

4 Repairs to internal enriched moulded
   work in situ   24
   Plaster columns and pilasters   24
   Enriched solid run cornices   25
   Running in solid plaster screeds   28
   Restoration of in situ mouldings to
   a curved background   28
   Handforming   30

5 Repair and replacement of mouldings
   in fibrous plaster   31
   Repairs to existing fibrous work   31
   Removal of existing fibrous work   31
   Construction of models   34
   Preparation of models   34
   Flood moulds   34
   Run case moulding   36
   Clay case mould   36
   Casting and fixing plain fibrous work   38
   Domework and intersecting curves   38
   Vaulting and lunettes   39
   Casting curved and enriched work   39
   New materials for mouldings   39

6 Repair and restoration of external
   plastering   41
   Formation of mitres, breaks and
   returns   44
   Ashlar and imitation stonemasonry   45
   On-site casting using OPC/sand   45
   GRC in restoration   46

7 Specialist work   48
   Composition   48
   Pargetting   48
   Scagliola   49

8 Faults   50
Bibliography   51

Appendix A   Specification of plastering
             work   52

Appendix B   Glossary of plastering terms   54

Appendix C   Specialist plasterers   58
             and suppliers

List of illustrations
Fig. 1 Internal plaster cornice running
         mould reverse   9
Fig. 2 Internal plaster cornice running
         mould solid   10
Fig. 3 Twin slippered running mould   14
Fig. 4 Three legged, half slippered
         running mould   16
Fig. 5 Multi-centred ellipses   17
Fig. 6 Portable trammel   18
Fig. 7 Peg mould and curved rule   20
Fig. 8 Enriched cornice   26
Fig. 9 Run loose piece reverse mould   29
Fig. 10 Running mould and run cast   32
Fig. 11 Plain moulded pilaster   33
Fig. 12 Enriched cornice model   35
Fig. 13 Exploded side view of an enriched
         truss   37
Fig. 14 External OPC/sand cornice
         running mould   41
Fig. 15 External moulding alternative
         method   42
Fig. 16 Metal bracketting external cornice 43

Authors' preface

We have written this book with a number of objectives in mind. Firstly, to assist the modern craftsman who may not have had the opportunity to work in traditional materials and methods, and who now finds himself in need of this knowledge. Secondly, to give an overview of the craft to the supervisor who is in charge of a restoration contract. Thirdly, to guide the architect and designer, who may need some knowledge of either traditional specification or its modern counterpart, and the feasibility of various operations concerning the use of solid or fibrous plasterwork when restoring decorative work. Finally, to help the owner or occupier of a listed building who may want to carry out small works himself, or to employ a general building contractor to perform the operation.

At no time does the book set out to be a general plastering textbook. In a book of this size, it is just not possible to cover everything. However, many basic exercises have been included and these, with the specialist examples, should enable readers to solve many of the problems arising from the restoration of antique plasterwork.

Don Stagg and Ron Masters
1983

Don Stagg, formerly Head of Department of Building Crafts at Hammersmith and West London College, taught plasterwork for over 30 years and was a CGLI examiner in the subject. His previous publications include:

with Brian Pegg
A Craftsman's Encyclopaedia
Collins 1976

Plastering Question and Answer
Butterworth 1978

Ronald Masters is lecturer in charge of the plastering department at Hammersmith and West London College.

1 Introduction to antique plasterwork

Materials and methods

Backgrounds

Whether considering modern plastering specifications or looking into methods of restoring antique plasterwork, the basic approach should be reasonably similar. What material has been used for the background? This can affect the choice of materials and the mix used for the backing coats. This in turn can have a similar effect upon the choice of materials for the finishing coat. A major cause of the breakdown of much of the old plastering in this country can be traced to one of two main faults. The first of these is the application of a hard brittle plaster finish to a softer, more friable backing coat. The second is the deterioration of the backing due to age, dampness or movement. Both of these faults can cause the finishing coat to flake away from the floating coat. On the other hand, the use of more modern materials on old backgrounds may cause different problems. Just a few years ago a recently restored riven wood lath ceiling became completely covered by small cracks. On checking the specification it was found that a strong ordinary Portland cement/sand mix had been used for the backing coats, while the finish was neat class C gypsum plaster. The first coat had gripped the laths so tightly that no movement was possible when the dry laths were saturated by the wet plaster. More water was added with the next coat, and when the ceiling dried out, the laths moved again and the result was mass cracking. A weaker mix would have allowed the small amount of movement necessary to take place within the plaster.

A strong gauged gypsum plaster/sand mix for backing coats may also cause problems unless expertly applied. The expansion that takes place when gypsum plaster sets can cause a breakdown of adhesion when applied to unsuitable backgrounds. Similarly strong finishes may well lift off a soft friable backing coat. Many materials have been used both to present the plasterer of the period with a background on which to perform and by him in the way of backing and finishing coats.

Wattle and daub is probably the oldest method of plastering known to be used in this country. It consisted of erecting a number of hard wood slats vertically and then interweaving horizontally with rods of hazel. To this mud or clay, reinforced with straw, was daubed internally and externally. Similar forms of construction are still in use in Third World countries with a predominantly rural population.

Apart from the more solid types of background, such as natural rock and stone, it is possible to see reeds, rushes, wood and metal laths and wire netting. As with all materials used in very old buildings, the local resources featured largely in the supply and usage. For the plasterer this was especially true, local limestone, sand and other materials influenced to a certain extent the amount of work that is still there for us to see today. A good lime (properly slaked and allowed to mature), mixed with a clean hard, sharp and gritty sand and a fibrous material, such as hair or sisal, then correctly applied and finished can survive for hundreds of years. Other additives were used from time to time and these can vary from road sweepings, manure, to ground marble. However, the substance that was used more than most, especially in external lime stucco, was glue size. This has the effect of hardening mixes that contain gypsum and, at the same time, retarding the set. Plasterers who have worked on the restoration of external antique plastering have found traces of what they consider to be gypsum plaster used in the finishing coat.

Solid backgrounds for plastering have always been stone, rocks, bricks, blocks and similar materials. For early ceilings and partitions, reed bales were used. These were bundles of reeds tied together with skin, other reeds, cord and, more recently, wire. The bundles were then laced or tied back to the building construction members with stronger cord or wire, forced back to a fairly flat surface then plastered with haired lime plaster. This type of background has not been used in this country for many years, but there is evidence to show that a similar method was used in one European country until quite recently. Once again, in both cases, builders used locally-produced materials which were easily obtainable.

For many years wood laths, in the form of split or riven laths, presented a background for plasterers work. These laths, sometimes of oak, other times of Red Baltic fir, were all made from knot-free, straight grained timber. The splitting was originally done by plasterers during the cold winter months. Plasterers would also carry out the bulk of the fixing which was by wrought or cast iron nails. These were later replaced by galvanized nails on work that was considered top quality. Local by-laws often included reference to the riven lath by stating that the deviation from the straight should not be greater than the full width of the lath, and that all timber should be free of sap.

Latterly, the riven lath was replaced by the sawn lath; these were all made from Baltic or North American timber. Today, wood laths are still used in great quantities as reinforcing and fixing members of fibrous plastering, but as a background to solid work only when specified. It is possible to get hold of split laths if required, but in general building the wood laths have been replaced by several other backgrounds.

All plastering to a wood lath background has to be a minimum of three coat work. A render coat of about 8–10 mm ($\frac{3}{8}$ in) was first applied across the lath work. This would be followed by a floating or straightening coat of the same thickness. Finally the finished coat of some 3 mm would be applied. Specific methods of keying would be carried out between coats, and a set time would be allowed to occur before application of the following coat. This will be discussed later in the book.

Forms of wire netting used as a substitute for wood laths in several countries date back to the mid-1800s and heralded the introduction of expanded metal lathing. This was very extensively used since it improved the fire resistance of plaster ceilings and partitions. It was also used to encase ironwork stanchions and to reinforce internal and external cornices. Later in the same century many patent metal laths appeared, all claiming to be the best available. From these most of today's metal laths were developed perforated, dovetailed, etc., and others disappeared completely.

Expanded metal lathing is used in vast quantities today and forms an excellent ceiling when plastered with the correct grade of premixed lightweight aggregate plaster.

Another type of lathing used years ago, and in some areas until the present day, is brick lath. This consisted of pliable wires interlaced to form small wire squares. At every intersection small pieces of burnt clay covered the wire on both sides. This burnt clay formed a similar material to the common brick of today. Therefore, brick lath formed a unique background of the lathing type as it gave a high suction surface.

Another type of background used in the past was the solid, gypsum plaster slab. These were made in size to either a square yard or smaller and to a thickness of 1 in (25 mm). During the casting process the slab mould would be filled halfway up and a double layer of plasterers' canvas pressed into the wet plaster. The mould was then filled to the top and ruled off perfectly flat. Just before the plaster set a stiff broom would be passed over it in a criss-cross fashion, forming a deep key. When set, the slabs could be fixed either way up or out. The smooth side formed a ready finished surface and the broomed side formed a keyed surface for normal two coat plastering.

The method used to cast these slabs was one gauge. This meant that the plaster was heavily retarded by the addition of size water. This also made the surface very hard and also fairly impervious to water penetration on the smooth side.

Suction

In modern times, the plasterer has to be prepared to work on very many backgrounds. To assist with the choice of materials for the plastering specification they are divided into two types: high suction and low suction. While the materials that a modern plasterer will use in new buildings will not rely upon suction for the set or hardening, adhesion will. This is one of the main differences between traditional and modern solid plastering. At one time, all solid plastering relied heavily upon background and backing coat suction. If the background provided little suction then the render coat had to fulfil that function. In the field of restoration work it is important to understand this.

To assist in the build up of sufficient suction for most solid plastering operations until the mid-1930s, three coat lime plastering appeared to be the rule. Raw lime hair mortar or plasterers' 'coarse stuff' was used for the render and floating coats. This consisted of one part lime to three parts sand with hair or sisal added to provide an additional adhesive quality. The amount of hair added was usually 1 lb of hair to every 3 ft^3 of mortar. At its heaviest it could be as much as 2 lb of hair to every 3 ft^3 of mortar.

Lime

The lime used on most sites was either pure or fat lime. It was slaked on site or at the plasterer's yard. Once thoroughly slaked and passed through a sieve it would be allowed to settle. The lime would settle to the bottom of the bin and water would form a protective barrier on top of the lime. The whole bin remained covered and left for a period of time, lasting from three weeks to several months. As long as the water remained as a protective barrier over the top, and stopped air from hardening the lime, the lime would remain in a plastic state. Similarly, the coarse stuff was often prepared in a purely traditional way. It would be 'layered', and this meant alternate layers of sand and lime being left exposed to the elements for several months, thereby maturing naturally. During dry weather it was saturated occasionally. Some people feel that one of the problems with present day plastering is that materials are no longer allowed to mature naturally.

Textbooks offer differing advice about the length of time that slaked lime should be left to mature. In England this appeared to vary from a maximum of nine months to the accepted three week period in the nineteenth century. The Romans required slaked lime to mature three years before use.

Sand

Sand can normally be obtained from three sources: the sea, rivers or pits. Good sand for plastering must be hard, sharp, gritty and free from all organic matter.

These qualities are essential and normally can only be found in first class pit sand. In general, river sand will be too even or 'soft', while sea sand may contain salt. This does not necessarily weaken the mix but can cause efflorescence. It also makes the mortar more liable to retain moisture. Today the practice is to use the well graded sands from reputable suppliers, whereas years ago a plasterer would order quantities of coarse and fine sands. These he would mix on site to get the correct grading; very coarse for undercoat work, less coarse for finishing.

Cement

Most of the cement work, whether internal or external, carried out by the plasterer today will be in Portland cement. This material was first patented in this country in the early part of the nineteenth century. Before this there were several cements in use of varying qualities and the only one which appears to have stood the test of time is Roman cement. This was introduced in the latter half of the eighteenth century and was extensively used for external plastering. It can be identified as it was normally brown in colour and resembled a cement used by the Romans. It set very quickly and could be used for casting in much the same way as plaster. However, it did not provide the same degree of strength that is available with the use of ordinary Portland cement (OPC).

Another material used many years ago was selenitic lime cement (or just plain 'selenitic'). Used for external work, or where a very hard undercoat was needed it consisted of lime of a hydraulic nature mixed with either sand or ground brick with about 5 per cent of gypsum plaster added at time of use. As a finishing material, chalk or fat lime could be used in place of hydraulic lime.

Stucco

Stucco is a term that originated in Italy and was usually applied to certain types of external plastering. In this country it does not have quite the same meaning. More often than not it applies to various mixes used by plasterers containing assorted ingredients including limes, aggregates, sometimes gypsum plasters, cements, Roman cement, selinitic and several other self-styled cements. These have all been superseded by ordinary Portland cement.

Many people have tried to find a way of describing the differences between stucco and plasterwork. One way, widely accepted, though not entirely accurate, is to say that stucco is lime-based while plasterwork is gypsum plaster-based. This, however, leads to further argument since many old examples of stucco contain a percentage of gypsum plaster.

Another way is to list the operations and mixes carried out in stucco. This method was used in England and the list included 'common stucco' prepared from hydraulic lime, sand and hair. This was an external material. 'Rough stucco' came next. Consisting of chalk or pure lime plus sand, it was used internally to imitate stonework. Colouring was added and various aggregates were substituted for sand. It was finished by felt float and, occasionally, a mason's drag to improve the stone effect. The third type was 'bastard stucco'; basically a very superior lime setting stuff prepared from fat lime putty and fine washed sand. This was applied to a good backing coat in another two or three coats, scoured and either polished or left floated, and was not painted. Finally, 'trowelled stucco'; this must have been the original lime setting stuff, applied as a normal finishing coat, scoured, polished and painted.

Much of the external plastering carried out in this country today is called stucco, a normal 1:1:6 OPC, lime, sand mix. Due to our climate pure lime stucco or gypsum plasters are not suitable for normal external work. Why is this? The lime mixes were used extensively many years ago. Is it because of the material preparation or the application? Did the old craftsmen use additives of their own to help repel water? Fine marble dust in hard trowelled work will do this. Certain glutinous materials have a similar effect. Problems occur when restoring this work especially if it does not have to be painted. This will be dealt with later in the book.

Fibrous plasterwork

Fibrous plasterwork has a shorter history than the solid aspects of plastering. Solid plastering can broadly follow the development of man, from the earliest mud hut dwellings and 'plastering' with bare hands to modern day techniques, which include the use of both traditional hand tools and mechanical tools, such as power floats and spray machines. The types of plaster available today include: acoustic, lightweight, multipurpose one coat plasters and X-ray plaster – a far cry from the earliest materials of mud and straw.

Fibrous plasterwork in historical terms can be traced back to the last century. The Frenchman L. A. Desachy took out a patent in 1856 with specifications for casting from reverse moulds, making lightweight reinforced casts and fixing and making good on-site.

Production and moulding

Methods of casting from reverse moulds had been in operation for centuries in one form or another. The moulds were very restrictive since the enrichment or sections required were confined to small works, for example bands of enrichments, motifs and plaques. Another restriction was that the model could not contain any undercut areas. The reason for this was that the casts could be removed from the mould with ease.

The earliest reverse moulds were formed in wood, lead, wax, clay and plaster. All of these materials, with the exception of clay, were rigid. When an undercut feature was desired on a cast, the craftsman carved out the area required by hand. Wax reverse moulds when correctly handled could produce casts with shallow undercuts. It was probably one of the earliest 'pliable' materials to be used for reproducing this type of cast.

Clay is another pliable material which was used in much the same way as the pressing of plasticine on to an object, and achieving the reverse shape. The reverse impression was filled with wet plaster to produce a copy of the original.

Reproducing works in the round, for example busts and statues, developed approximately 600 years ago. This method of moulding is known as 'piece moulding'. The art of the 'piece moulder' was and still is an exact one. A reverse mould is slowly constructed from pieces cast on the model. Each piece is designed to be removed from the undercut area, and also to be interlocking with each other, together with an overall smooth back, all of which can be held together with a plaster case or back. The back and pieces form an integrated reverse mould from which copies of the original can be produced. Italy seems to have been the place where the art of piece moulding was developed and Michelangelo was credited with the mastering of this skill.

The use of reverse moulds for the reproduction of enrichments and ornaments during the mid-eighteenth century slowly became standardized. Sections which had previously been carved and moulded with great expertise *in situ* were now moulded from one original model. The interpretation of design, and the artistic qualities of the craftsman was slowly but surely being eliminated.

This trend of reproducing sections continued into the next century, during which experiments with materials to develop a flexible mould were tried and tested. Finally, during the late 1840s Mr J. Herbert, a modeller, produced an undercut cast from a gelatine mould.

Gelatine

By the 1851 Paris Exhibition, the problems of using gelatine for multiple castings were overcome and, at the exhibition, casts of plaques, busts and statues were being produced. The new material, gelatine, gradually superseded to some degree the use of plaster back and front moulds, piece moulds, and waste moulds as a means of obtaining the undercut cast. It also removed the time-consuming work of carving out the undercut sections.

With the new concept of forming reverse moulds of enriched features there were immediate problems to overcome. The main problem was to control the setting time of the plaster more accurately, and the preparation of the mould.

Examples of use

Because casting plaster generates heat and expands when it sets the casts which were allowed to stay in a gelatine reverse mould melted the face of the mould, and so caused a serious deterioration of the intended detail. Gelatine has a low melting point, around 110–120°F (45°C). As it is a soft material, excessive 'brushing-in' of the plaster over its surface can also damage the moulded face. Once these problems were successfully eradicated, the art of fibrous plasterwork was well and truly developing into the specialist area of plastering that we know today.

During the latter part of the nineteenth century and the early part of the twentieth century, the mechanics of moulding, casting and fixing fibrous work improved. The material was unique because combined with its flexibility and lightness it also contained fire-resistant qualities; these qualities made fibrous plaster an ideal and safe medium to use in public buildings. In this period fibrous work was used extensively in the refurbishing of old theatres and was also used to decorate the new cinema buildings which were in their infancy in the early part of this century.

The cinemas provided an excellent opportunity to experiment with designs. Interior design work gradually developed from the basic essentials of a large hall containing seats, into buildings with elaborate styles of ornate and flamboyant works. The range of decoration ranged from neo-classical to the then revolutionary art deco styles. The areas of work included the main auditorium and foyers. In the auditorium for instance the main features were the proscenium arch, balcony fronts and soffits, cornice and frieze work. The ceiling areas could contain various types and shapes of domed work, enriched coffered beam sections and segmental work. The wall decoration varied in design from plain walls and panel moulding sections to columns, pilasters and arches.

The manufacture of fibrous work can be planned and scheduled well in advance in the 'fibre shop' or factory. It can then be stored, and transported to the building site when required, thereby saving valuable 'on-site' time and, possibly, contributing to earlier completion dates by using the existing workforces effectively and efficiently.

Precast plaster work is not only an ideal material to produce an illusion of grandeur and splendour but also proves itself a first class product with which to incorporate the necessary services of the building, for example heating and ventilation, lighting, signwork, and alarm systems. One good example mentioned earlier is the proscenium arch. While naturally providing the focal point of attention in the auditorium, the arch also conceals stage and screen lighting, loudspeaker systems, and heating and ventilation units. It therefore has a multi-purpose role in addition to being an integral part of the whole interior design.

Worth mentioning are two cinemas which are excellent examples of the very different styles of design used in the 1930s. They are the Granada Tooting in South London with its splendid traditional designs including coffered ceilings, moulded beam work, and the superbly decorated walls of the auditorium; and the ACE (formerly Odeon) Cinema at Rayners Lane in North London which is now a listed building. The style of decoration at this cinema is art deco. The foyer and auditorium ceilings provide the main design work and consists of long sweeping curves of lighting troughs and reflector coves.

Throughout Britain in all the large cities and towns where there is an old cinema or theatre, some form of decorative plasterwork will probably be in evidence. Hopefully the design work is still being appreciated by the general public, whether the building is still being used for its original purpose, or has been converted.

Another source of fibrous plasterwork included the great exhibitions and expositions which were being staged throughout the world. The individual manufacturers' stands and the national pavilions could be built to the most lavish and outrageous designs.

At the British Empire Exhibition in 1924 and 1925, held at Wembley in North London, there were many examples of fibrous work. They ranged from reproductions of Burmese carvings which were used to supplement the original work to the magnificent example of the Indian pavilion which was a scaled down replica of the Taj-Mahal. This was constructed of 'steel and fibrous plasterwork', and was situated in the open air. The decorators must have used many hundreds of gallons of lead paint to render the normally porous fibrous surface impermeable to the British weather conditions.

Among numerous items exhibited in the British pavilion at the Brussels World Fair 1958 was a fibrous plaster reproduction of the west window in Westminster Abbey.

In the British pavilion at Expo 1967 held in Montreal, there was a great deal of fibrous plasterwork. Although the designs were plain and without enrichments, the shapes demanded a great deal of skill to construct. These included large plain circular columns and an elaborate elliptical escalator surround which lead into a cavern-shaped hall (totally formed in fibrous plaster) in which were housed giant human-shaped figures (again in fibrous work). All the work was moulded and cast by many firms in the London area, then packed in crates and transported by ship to Montreal, for fixing and making good.

In more recent years the type of exhibition setting and styles have changed, accommodating the newer materials and techniques constantly being developed. This means that the once dominant fibrous plasterwork is gradually being superseded.

One area where the 'exhibition type' of fibrous plasterwork is still being used is in the film industry. The film studios at Pinewood in Buckinghamshire, and at the EMI Studios in Borehamwood, Hertfordshire, are still constructing large sets for film and television.

Recently a large scale reproduction of the facade of Notre Dame Cathedral was planned from the scale drawings. Reverse moulds were made and casts from these were used to reconstruct the building's outer face. Small scale models and interior work are also used to create the impression of reality in the new space film epics, for example *Star Wars* and *Star Trek*.

In the post-war period from the 1950s onwards there was a great deal of fibrous plasterwork used in the restoration of many historical buildings which were damaged during World War II. One area in particular which provided a first class challenge to the country's architects, designers and craftsmen, was the City of London's churches, many of which were part of the 'new London' designed by Sir Christopher Wren after the Great Fire of 1666. These churches were rich in architectural features and ornamentation. In many cases complete new interiors had to be designed from existing drawings, plans and photographs. Whenever possible the existing features were used to form the basis of the intended reproduction work, ensuring that the new work would follow the original designs as closely as possible. Some very good examples of this type of work are St. Brides in Fleet Street, St. Clement Danes in the Strand and St. Vedast in Foster Lane.

Fibrous plasterwork is still being produced to form decorative surfaces. In the majority of large construction projects, for example office blocks, airport terminals, schools and churches, etc., the style is towards plain-face work, with clean cut angles and curved work, providing the features that are reminiscent of the art deco work of the 1920s and 1930s.

Once again, the fire-resisting and non-toxic qualities of fibrous plaster have provided designers with an ideal medium with which to shape and decorate.

The reproduction of the distinctive architectural periods such as Tudor, Classical 'Wren' Renaissance, Georgian, Regency, Victorian and, more recently, the Edwardian period, are still appreciated. Many hotels, restaurants, dance halls and private houses, whether these are newly built or being refurbished, are being transformed with expertly designed plasterwork to a style or period that will enhance the buildings.

PVC

Changes have once again taken place in the reproduction of undercut enriched features. As previously mentioned, a major drawback when using gelatine reverse moulds for casting was its delicate constitution and the need for skilled attention and care at all times. Despite using all the necessary skills, gelatine still has a limited life in its reverse mould form. With continual melting and wear and tear it gradually lost a good deal of its moulding qualities and flexibility. In the late 1940s a new pliable material, polyvinyl chloride, better known as PVC, was developed. Once again, there were teething problems, for example in the preparation of the model from which the PVC reverse mould was to be obtained. When the new heating and moulding techniques had been mastered, the days of the gelatine moulds were numbered.

2 Internal plain surfacing

The planning of all repair work to old plastering, whether internal or external, should follow five recommended stages. These rules can be applied in almost any circumstances when dealing with restoration work. The preliminary stage would consist of a thorough inspection. This would show just how much of the old plastering would need replacing, type of materials required and thicknesses. After the careful removal of the damaged work a similarly thorough inspection of the background would be necessary. Is it sound? What preparation is necessary or should it be removed completely? The next stage is the material check. Does the specification demand the use of traditionally prepared materials or does it allow for either the substitution of modern counterparts or even the use of suitable new materials? Next the application must be considered. Should the plastering be in one, two or three coats? What levels are necessary and how can it be applied without disturbing or damaging the existing work? Finally, we arrive at the finish – hard or soft, smooth or textured?

Stage one, the inspection   Tests must be made to check on just how much of the existing work needs to be replaced. Fairly gentle taps will indicate how much of the plaster has parted company with its background. The indications will generally be in two ways: a hollow sound or movement. The ear soon becomes familiar with the appropriate sound, and errors in judgement will disappear. Test holes may be gently drilled where any doubt exists, or a series of holes drilled so that an area of work can be removed.

Once the extent of the damage has been identified removal can take place. Whether it is a large area, a wall or ceiling, large patch or small patch, care must be taken. The background should not be damaged and sound plastering must not be loosened. Cut large areas into sections by using a full blade of an old saw on the face of the plaster. If necessary, arrange pads and props under or against the old work. This will prevent the loosened work from crashing down, and the sound work from being parted from its background. To let an unskilled casual workman 'cut loose' with a hammer will cause at least two problems. Firstly, a major dust storm and, secondly, damage to existing work.

Even when preparing smaller areas it is always best to use a saw as it will at least provide straight edges. When all the old work has been removed, cut back all of the edges to provide an undercut section. This will greatly assist in holding the new plaster in place. Also, these same edges should be treated. Many years ago a skilled plasterer working on such an operation would have at his disposal a tin of old lead-based paint. The edges of the old plastering would be treated with this for two

reasons. Firstly, it would stabilize the existing work and make for better adhesion. Secondly, it would prevent the spread of water into the existing work, thus preventing staining. When working on the old lath backgrounds, as much as is possible of the old dust and dirt on the back of the lath must be removed. Should the edges not be treated and the dust not be removed, the water will spread into the old work both softening and combining with the old dust to cause staining. Today, a good PVA adhesive will be just as effective and should be carefully applied to all edges.

Stage two, the background   In most old buildings the background will probably be one of four materials: stone or brick; reeds or wood laths. A more recent building may contain metal lathing.

Problems that can occur on the solid backgrounds are soundness or solidity and facing erosion. Is the wall constructionally sound? Does it move? Are the blocks loose? If it is sound, has the facing of the brick, block or stone flaked or is it in the process of flaking? If the wall is generally unsound it must be replaced. Plaster will not hold a building up! If the background is reasonably sound the next stage is treatment. A good wire brushing will reveal and remove loose particles; and a soft broom or brush will remove dust. Finally, the background will need a good dampening. Should any doubt exist concerning adhesion then a spatterdash coat is recommended. This will consist of OPC and sharp sand 1:2 applied to the background with an old water brush or, alternatively, a PVA adhesive may be used. Both of these will cut out all suction therefore making the use of a raw coarse stuff backing unsuitable. A 1:1:6 or a 1:$\frac{1}{2}$:4 mix consisting of OPC or gypsum plaster, lime and sand (in that order) would be reasonable. A 1:2:8 mix could even be used. For small areas 1:3 or 4 of class A plaster and sand would be reasonable for the backing coats, with the finish being 50:50 class A plaster and lime putty. The larger areas would be governed by specification for all coats.

Wood lath backgrounds require even more careful attention. As the old riven laths were usually made from oak they might still be in excellent condition. Therefore, when removing old plastering it is even more important to have a skilled craftsman to do the easing down. A heavy unskilled hand will probably ensure that the laths will need replacing as well! Very often re-nailing will be required where the old lath nails have rusted away or have been pulled through the lath. Where the specification states that riven laths must be used to replace damaged ones they should be nailed to every joist and spaced about 8 mm apart. Where an alternative background is permitted, metal lathing will be the best since it is possible to get near to the old thickness of plaster with it. Plasterboard will only be suitable for small areas where it could be nailed over the laths or on a large area if the thicker or the laminated system could be used. On a wood lath background a 1:1:6 or 1:$\frac{1}{2}$:4 mix with cattle hair or sisal would be suitable.

Old reed ceilings have been found still in reasonable condition, when unaffected by dampness. In most cases, however, they are removed and replaced by metal laths. A lot of background preparation may be necessary, however, if the specification demands that the reeds be replastered. All old plaster must be removed as well as dust and dirt on the facework and the back. The bales may need rewiring in the individual bundles as well as refixing to the timber supports. This is done using galvanized tying wire. It is also recommended that the area to be plastered is covered by galvanized chicken wire. Once again, this is laced, tied and stapled to all supports and to the reed ties. A well haired 1:1:6 mix is best on this background, applied as backing coats in at least two or more applications. The finishing to this would be a 4:1 lime setting stuff, class A gypsum mix.

Metal lath ceilings are usually the easiest to restore as, in most cases, the background will need replacing as well. From personal experience with this background, it is quite common to find the wire has almost completely rusted away. Ceilings like this show just why the plasterer of that period insisted on using so much hair or sisal. It had probably been keeping the ceiling up!

Stage three, the materials In much of the preceding text we have mentioned some materials and mixes. Some of the materials used for restoration and repair work will come in ready-mixed form. Does it nevertheless pay the plasterer to go back to making up his own traditional mixes? Some of the work which can be seen in historic buildings is still sound. Is this because of the materials used, or the quality of workmanship at the time of construction? Will new materials equally stand the test of time? In general, materials available today are perfectly satisfactory. The rest is down to personal preference.

Sand is another important factor in modern plastering. Many years ago plasterers would mix various types of sand on site until they obtained the best grade to suit the job. Add to this the fact that the lime mixed with the sand was well matured, naturally slaked lime putty and you may have at least one reason for the old plastering lasting so well, although the application counted too.

Today, we have an excellent system for grading our sands, but can we rely upon the specification being adhered to? There have been occasions when plasterers have refused to use the specified grade of sand for the job because they found it too sharp. Sharp sand can make

the practical application more difficult than a cream sand and it may cut down on the bonus earned! Fortunately, this does not happen too often on restoration sites.

There are several additives that are now used, most of them with OPC/sand mixes and, with a reduced lime content, they still improve the workability of the mix. Hair, sisal and tow are all in use today and are still obtainable. Colouring agents, suction controllers and waterproofing compounds have all been used in restoration work and as these are all proprietary brands, the manufacturer's instructions should be read carefully.

Several new materials have also been introduced. Premixed plasters and patent finishes all have some advantages, but there are pitfalls to look out for, for instance where the thickness of the plastering exceeds the recommended thicknesses of the premixed plasters. In this case 'dubbing out' should be applied in additional coats of a stronger mix and in several thin coats.

Stage four, the application Two rules should be followed for all solid plastering; always float from right to left; and always finish from left to right – this applies to right-handed plasterers. Most plasters are much better for adding or applying in several thin coats rather than building out in one. Thin coats make for better adhesion and plastering applied in this manner will generally crack less.

When using gauged or raw lime plasters a wooden lath scratcher should always be used as it gives the keying an undercut section. A comb or wire scratcher will not do that. It is only necessary to key undercoats that are to receive another heavy undercoat in this fashion. Floating coats should always be keyed by the application of a devil float.

The application of raw lime plasters, 'coarse stuff' and 'setting stuff', will be heavily reliant upon suction for hardening. A period of not less than three weeks is usual between all coats. This means that the render coat will be more or less bone-dry before the floating coat is applied. The suction from the render coat, plus the undercut keying from the lath scratcher, will make for excellent adhesion. It is, however, essential for a fibrous material, such as hair, to be included in the mix. The floating coat must also be allowed three weeks or more to dry before the setting or finishing coat is applied. When this final coat is applied in a raw state, lime putty and fine washed sand, it should follow the trowel float, trowel pattern, three coats each about 1 mm thick. As the suction causes it to dry out the entire area should be 'hard scoured'. This is done by sprinkling water on by brush then rubbing a flat cross grain float over the area

Fig.1

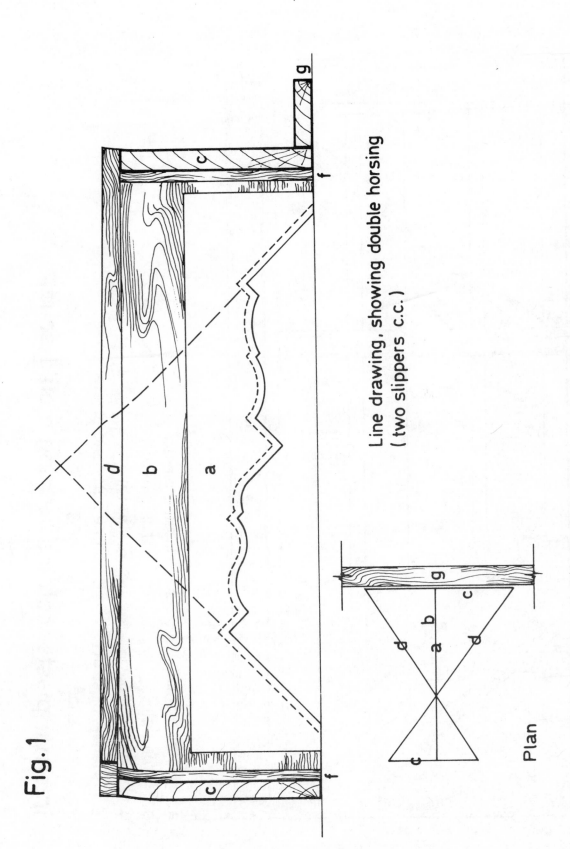

Line drawing, showing double horsing (two slippers c.c.)

Plan

Internal plaster cornice running mould reverse

Fig. 2

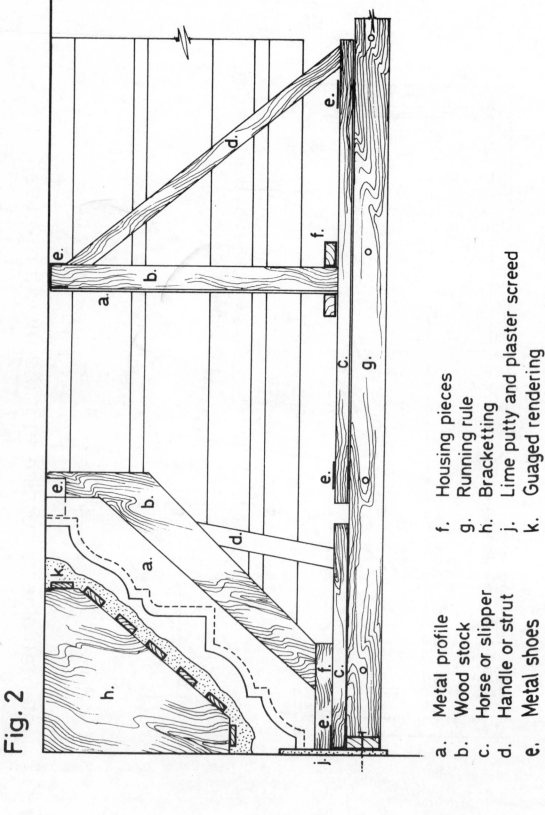

a.   Metal profile
b.   Wood stock
c.   Horse or slipper
d.   Handle or strut
e.   Metal shoes

f.   Housing pieces
g.   Running rule
h.   Bracketting
j.   Lime putty and plaster screed
k.   Guaged rendering

Internal plaster cornice running mould solid

in circular motions. This will bring 'lime fat' to the surface which in turn should be trowelled off. This *must* be removed. It will only crack if left on. Subsequent trowellings will close the setting coat surface and eventually result in a smooth polished lime plaster face ready for decoration.

Points to watch for when using lime plasters are as follows: the mixes, coarse stuff must be 1:3 lime putty and sand, plus hair, from 5 kg up to 10 or even 15 kg per m^3. When applied to any form of lath work it must be pushed through the key or gap between the laths. This is best done by working *across* the laths. The render coat should be no thicker than 10 mm and no less than 8 mm from the face of the lath. The key, whether formed by a lath scratcher or a comb scratcher, must never expose the background. Thicknesses will remain the same for most backgrounds. The floating coat will be ruled off to previously applied screeds of the same material and to the same thickness. The keying of this coat will be by 'devil float', a wooden float with four small nails driven through the back in each corner until they project from the face of the float by 2–3 mm. As the floating coat hardens, the float face is laid flat on to the plaster surface and rotated. As well as keying, the float will also flatten the ruled in surface and help to bind it. Just before the setting coat is applied the floated surface should be lightly brushed free from dust and then dampened.

When the plastering is OPC or gypsum plaster gauged lime plasters, the application is exactly the same except for the time between coats, which can be as little as twenty-four hours. The mix should range from 1:1:6 down to a stronger 1:$\frac{1}{2}$:4, that is, unless a class 3 undercoat plaster is being used, in which case the mix will vary according to the background and the manufacturer's recommendations. The old-fashioned gypsum undercoat plasters are not readily available today but we are told that the modern counterparts are as good.

One way round this is to use the fibrous plasterer's method of retarding the set of class A gypsum plaster. He will use a liquid form of glue size to slow down the set. This is added to the gauging water. The method is never as accurate on site as it is in the workshop. This is due to either dirty water, impurities in the sand or the method used to mix up. However, it is possible to get a reasonably good idea of the setting time.

There have been occasions when the specification has permitted the use of lightweight premixed plasters. Undercoats have been developed to suit any type of background, while the finish is standard on all backings. These will all appear in the specification table in Appendix A.

The application of lightweight plaster is basically as for any other gauged plasters. Each plaster manufactured is readily identified with its correct background, browning for high suction, bonding for low suction and metal lathing for all backgrounds that contain any metal. Thicknesses for backing coats vary from 8 to 10 mm while the finishing coat should be 2 mm thick. There is nothing wrong in using these plasters in restoration work, though, of course, they do not conform to the original specification.

Once again the application can affect the final results. Poorly applied backing coats will crack and adhesion will break down. This may be caused by a poorly prepared background, the individual coat application being too thick and applied too gently, or the adulteration of materials. Ineffective ruling in on the floating coat and the lack of keying by devil float can also cause poor quality finish. The finish coat can be polished and in many ways is better for it, but check on the type of paint that is to be applied.

The final point – the finish, hard or soft It shows really how far away from the old ideas we are when today one is generally advised to consider raw lime setting stuff as a 'soft finish'. When the lime putty was mixed with good clean fine washed sharp sand, and then properly applied, scoured and polished, it formed a really hard polished surface for the decorators. In fact how many times have people said that when pulling down plasterwork of, say, a hundred years old, once through the hard skin of the finish, the backing coat just crumbled away? To achieve this the mix must be right and the application correct.

The use of class C gypsum plaster (Sirapite) to form a harder surface followed much later, as did Keene's cement (class D plaster). Both of these plasters required the same method of application: three coats, scouring and polishing. Scouring is only possible and only achieves its objectives with gypsum plasters that have a slow continuous set. The snap or flash set of class B plasters do not respond to scouring. Polishing the final coat of plaster is not considered a desirable background for modern paints. The old paints would soak into the plasters and form a good base for future coats. Modern paints tend to form a skin over the plaster. Polishing the surface can cause adhesion problems. Therefore, check up on the paint that is to be used. Premixed lightweight gypsum plasters are typical of this type of soft 'soak-up' backing for the painter.

To sum up on the hard and soft finish, lime plasters will supply a generally soft finish unless mixed with sharp sand and hard scoured. Class C gypsum plaster is probably the only traditional hard finish plaster left, although it is not as hard as it used to be. Several modern finishes, some gypsum-based, some resin-based, others lime-based, all provide very specialized finishes and the maker's advice and instructions should be followed. Class B gypsum plaster is a medium hard finish when used neat and the premixed lightweight plaster is basically a soft finish.

Texture

Textures tend to be float finish or dab style finish. The finish should be applied as for a smooth finish but with irregular strokes to provide the 'olde' look. The dabbing may be done by using either a laying trowel or a gauging trowel. Twig dashing or brushing is another traditional finish. Hair or sisal was sometimes added to the finishing materials, not just to help in the binding, but to provide a basis for a stranded texture. Rollers of cloth or sacking produced rough textures, but one very fine texture was produced by pressing decorative French lace into the soft surface of the setting coat.

One failing of float, sponge or roller textures with lime plasters is that the hard polished surface is missing. Therefore, the result will be rather softer and extremely porous. In other European countries other aggregates more readily available were often used within the lime to give additional hardness. Crushed and powdered marble was a favourite in Italy and part of France, but mainly it was a combination of good basic materials and very good craftsmanship. The work had to be planned to the last detail, thus eliminating wastage.

A few additional points applied to general restoration work should be considered at this point. Plastering applied to any background must rely on adhesion, either to the background or to the backing coats, to be successful. Therefore any idea that can assist in this way must be worth considering. One method of helping adhesion to suspect backgrounds is to use the method mentioned when preparing reed backgrounds. Nail or staple a galvanized wire over the entire background face. This is used externally in many areas now as a basic necessity when repairing old external cement renderings. The wire may be galvanized chicken wire, metal lathing or a form of weld mesh.

The next problem is the thickness of coats. Lime plasters, raw or gauged, must never exceed 10 mm for each backing coat. When using premixed lightweight plasters the backing thicknesses may be similar but should a greater thickness be necessary then a stronger OPC/sand 'dubbing' out coat should be applied, again in thin coats of about 8–10 mm and each coat being well keyed. Finish coats in lime are up to 3 mm and in gypsum plasters 2 mm, others 3 mm.

3 Preparatory work

General principles

Internal moulded work will probably be repaired in one of two ways. Taking the first way, the specification will either demand or ask for all work to be restored in much the same way as the original. This will mean that the bulk of the work will be replaced '*in situ*'; mouldings run in position and enrichment and ornament cast and bedded. In the second way, for a number of reasons, such as excess weight, time, cost and practicability, the restored moulded work may well all be in fibrous precast plaster.

To the first method, the removal of the old plaster mouldings can be most important. A few gentle pulls, prods and taps will reveal just how much of the old work is loose. This must be removed carefully by cutting into short lengths by handsaw and easing down. It is possible that safe gathering of the old work may help in two ways. Firstly, it may well provide all the details for preparing the necessary running mould or moulds. Secondly, from the damaged sections it should be possible to piece together enough of the enrichment or ornament to make up a complete model with all repeats necessary for reproduction purposes. This does not limit itself to work in fibrous plaster either as in the days before this existed a plasterer would frequently prepare models so that he could obtain a reverse mould in plaster, wax, sulphur, clay, plasticine or, more latterly, gelatine on-site. This mould would be used to provide individual casts that could be bedded into especially run and prepared plaster beds within the run sections.

Where these conditions do not exist, for example all the damaged work may have been removed, then a 'squeeze' must be taken from the existing mouldings. This is necessary to obtain the true shape of the moulding so that the metal profiles may be produced to form the running moulds.

A squeeze to a section clear of enrichment may be taken in several ways. Traditionally, class A gypsum plaster would be splashed on to a cleaned and oiled strip of the moulding running from the projection to wall line in a cornice, thus encompassing the entire girth. The strip would be no wider than 50 mm and could be reinforced by the use of canvas. When this set hard, it was removed and showed a perfect profile that could be transferred to paper. A more up-to-date method is to obtain a square cut right through the moulding into which a piece of white card is placed. The section may then be traced on to the white card by following the outline of the cornice with a soft pencil. This method may also be used where the damaged mouldings have been cut down, thus exposing good clean sections at the end or ends.

Where enrichment exists, then modelling clay or plasticine may be pressed into the enrichment and plaster is splashed over the plain members also forming a backing for the clay. When transferring the section from this squeeze to paper a note is made of the enriched portions and beds are cut in the metal so that the enrichment can be bedded in after the moulding has been run.

All running moulds have a basic similarity in so far as they generally have a number of parts that have the same name. The metal profile will be either an exact replica of the moulding when going to be used to run a reverse mould or, when to run *in situ*, it will be the negative (see Figures 1 and 2). This in all cases will be strengthened and supported by a wooden stock or backing piece. A piece of 19 mm timber or plywood is cut 3 mm bigger than the moulding profile so that when correctly fixed, the metal will project 3 mm in front of the wood. The wood stock will be housed into either one or two wooden slippers placed at the end or ends of the stock and usually at right angles to it. The whole is then braced by suitable timber that will serve as handles as well as struts. Solid or *in situ* moulds may also be protected against wear at three points. A metal shoe is usually bent over the nib and nailed into the sides of the stock while the same type of shoe may be placed, one at either end of the slipper. These points are the main bearing points and the metal may need replacing after several full scale operations.

It is essential to thoroughly clean all old existing work at the point at which a squeeze is to be taken. Age and many coats of paint can distort plaster mouldings rather badly. For the metal profile it is best to use sheet tin as this is stronger than zinc, though the latter is frequently favoured as it is easier to file. There are several methods of transferring the section to the metal from the paper. One method is just to glue the paper on to the metal, another is to set the whole profile out on the metal using engineers' scribes and compasses. A third method is to pierce the paper at regular intervals around the entire girth of the moulding with a sharp point, making certain that the point marks the metal at each perforation. When complete, it should be possible to follow the pierce marks on the metal thus forming the cornice outline. Whichever method is used, once the drawing is satisfactory, one should use sharp tinmen's metal snips to cut as near to the line as possible. When complete, place the metal between two pieces of protective wood and then into a vice so that an accurate shape may be produced by the use of several different shaped files. The completed metal profile is then nailed to the stock which has been cut out by a bow or coping saw. A housing for the stock and profile is usually formed on the wooden slipper by nailing two pieces of batten on to the slipper

Fig.3   Twin slippered running mould

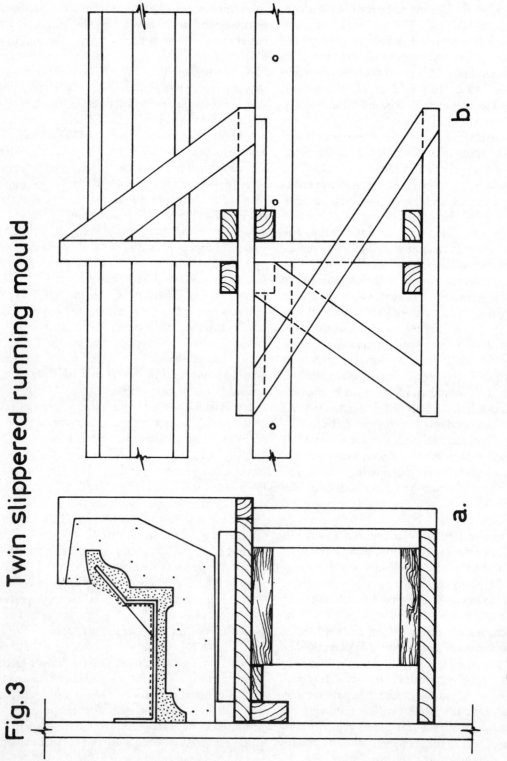

a.   Side view of mould in position
b.   Front

so that they will form a house or groove at the centre point to the length of the slipper. It is usual in industrial practice to nail running moulds together. However, under certain conditions and for restoration work we feel that it may be better to screw the mould together, the reasons being that it is easier to dismantle and store the moulds should they be required at a future date. Nailed running moulds invariably split when being dismantled.

Having got our moulds for casting enrichment (the methods for obtaining these moulds will be fully explained in the following section along with the running mould), it is preparation to the backing which we must now look at. It must be sound and strong enough to provide adhesive qualities, and soft friable plasters must be cut back to a good hard backing.

The ends of existing mouldings should be well keyed and treated with a neat PVA adhesive. This will prevent a breakdown and stop the spread of water into the old work. Running rules are needed and these will be fixed to the wall in such a position so that when the running mould slipper is placed on to it the new moulding will match up to the old, both in shape and in line. Masking out or the covering up of adjacent existing work may also be essential.

For large solid plaster mouldings, especially cornices, bracketing may be required. These are pieces of cut and impregnated timber either nailed to the sides of wooden joists or, where the joists run in the same direction as the cornice, fixed at right angles to the wall to noggin pieces that have been wedged and nailed between wall and joist. To the shaped face of the bracketing sections, wood or metal lathing is nailed and this in turn is rendered with a coat of either haired or fibrous material, reinforced gauged lime plaster (coarse stuff). Should this not be available, then a gypsum plaster/sand mix should be used, again reinforced by the addition of hair, sisal or tow. The render coat must be well keyed, using either a lath or wire scratcher, depending upon the size of the moulding.

Following this operation will be a 'muffle' run. A muffle is a 'false' or temporary profile made of hardboard, plywood, metal or hand-carved set plaster. The shape of the muffle will be as near as possible to that of the finished profile and when in position it will project 5–6 mm in front of the metal profile. A mixture of either gypsum plaster and coarse stuff or plaster and sand is then laid over the rendered bracketing. The running mould complete with the muffle is then run over the cornice length and the result will be a well 'cored' out moulding, the muffle run providing a perfect backing for the final run.

At the beginning of this chapter it was suggested that moulded work may be re-run as the original or cast in fibrous plaster, and the same can be said of the background. Is it always necessary to actually match as closely as possible the original work? There are two conflicting views in all restoration work, especially when it comes to plastering. One point of view says 'Yes! We must always replace and restore as near to the original as possible'; the other view suggests, 'Why not use modern materials and leave the comparisons to history?' Nothing has come forward to replace lime putty and plaster for solid run internal mouldings, though in some areas the modern premixed lightweight gypsum plasters have been used to run plain mouldings with some success. In fact, by using the method mentioned previously, the muffle run, with a backing of premixed bonding plaster and just 2-3 mm thickness of finish, some people feel that this could be the answer for the small modern cavetto style mouldings. However, whether or not this would prove as successful with the larger more classical style mouldings is a vastly different matter. Neither would it be suitable for casting and planting. The material does not harden sufficiently when fully set and is inclined to crumble when used for casting.

Although the method used to produce a running mould has been covered in rather general terms, it must be said that part of the training of a skilled craftsman is to have the ability and knowledge to identify the type of running mould for the operation in hand. A solid cornice mould would differ from, say, an architrave mould. This in turn would differ in shape to that of an angle bead or skirting mould. However, the basic principles would remain; a metal profile, a wood stock, the slipper or slippers, complete with struts and handles. When curved work is necessary a decision must be made whether to spin on a gig stick from a central pivot or whether to run on a curved rule using either a peg mould or a shaped slipper. These decisions would have to be made by the craftsman on-site as there are no real rules that could be applied in general and one would have to be knowledgeable about the many types of running mould that can be made up to suit the occasion.

In much the same way the method of running will be as described but there are many possible permutations to suit the varied operations. Also it is possible to vary methods to suit materials and mixes. However, the basic method should remain fairly stable. Never apply a too greater thickness at one time. Always key backing coats and never use a much stronger mix as a finish on a weak backing. Think the operation through before starting off.

One aspect of preparatory work is the removal of paint from original plaster mouldings. There are times when this is best left alone, for example when the bulk of

Fig. 4 Three legged, half slippered running mould

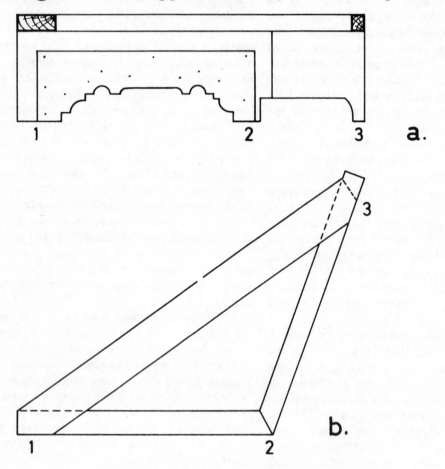

a. Front view of running mould
b. Plan of running mould
c. View from the slipper, showing the three bearing points

Multi-centred ellipses

Fig. 5

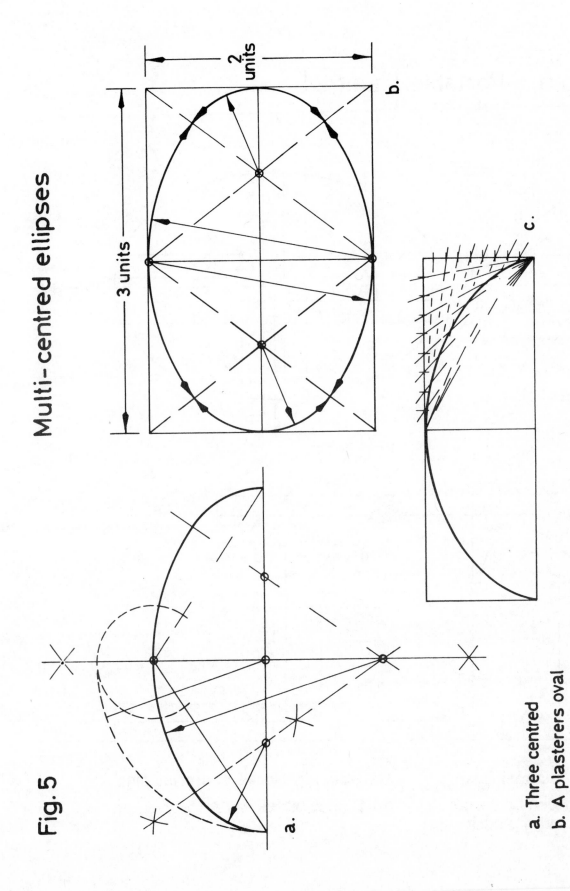

a. Three centred
b. A plasterers oval
c. Free hand curve to radiating lines

Fig.6   Portable trammel

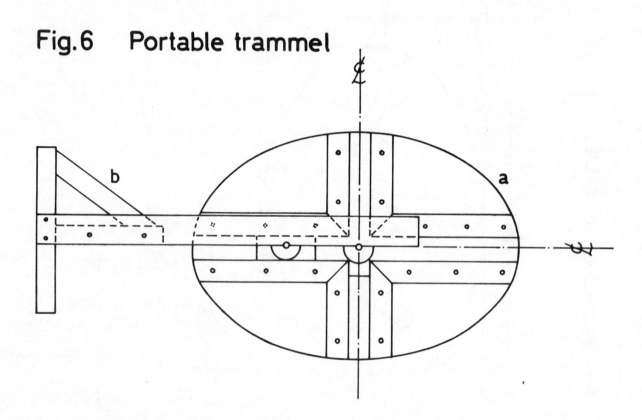

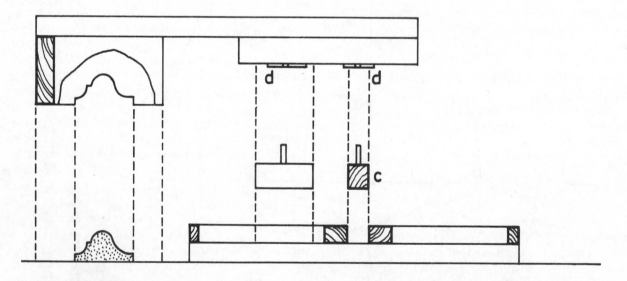

a. Trammel board
b. Running mould
    and gig-stick

c. Sliding blocks and pivot pins
d. Pivot plates

the work is in its original state. Should removal be essential then extreme caution is necessary. Paint strippers can be of great assistance, but some of these can affect the actual plaster.

Running moulds

One of the most important aspects in restoration and reproduction work for the skilled craftsman is probably not fully appreciated. It is the ability to be able to construct and use a variety of types of running mould.

As we have seen, all running moulds are basically the same in construction, i.e. a metal working profile supported by a wooden stock, which in turn is fixed at an angle of 90° to a wooden slipper. The two items are kept in the correct position with the aid of struts or braces. Apart from running off 'the comparatively simple tasks', such as reverse moulds and straight lengths of panel moulding. The more 'complicated' areas of forming mouldings with gig-sticks and eccentric rules are also to be established, constructed and then finally executed.

Some examples of different types of running mould are as follows. A twin-slippered running mould would be used for running sections of mouldings above window heads, door openings and forming lighting trough sections *in situ* (Figure 3). This type of running mould has two slippers on the same side of an extended stock, with a convenient distance between them. This will give the mould a good bearing and add support when running against the wall. This type of mould is used where the nib section has no surface to bear against.

Another variation of the running mould is a double-hinged mould which has two slippers, one on either end of the stock. The slippers are fixed to the stock with a hinge on the face of the stock and a slipper. The other hinge is fixed on the back of the stock and to the other slipper, thereby allowing the running mould to change its basic shape as it is drawn down the tapering sets of running rules.

When running mouldings *in situ* on a curved background, a half-slippered peg mould is used. The construction of this mould is very different from the others previously mentioned in that the stock is fixed at the front of the half-slipper (Figure 4). The bench line of the slipper will have the majority of its length removed leaving the two ends acting as bearing points, and the nib section of the stock acting as a bearing point. (This gives the mould its name three-legged half-slipper.) The three legs are trimmed to size to allow the mould to be run over the curved surface with the minimum of errors.

The position of the slipper to the stock is generally less than 90°, but exact position is determined by trial and error during practice runs. This mould can be used with either a hinged gig-stick for radius spinning on curved backgrounds or run against a curved or straight running rule.

The types of running mould mentioned above are only a few of the many that could be covered, but they will give the reader some idea of the complexities that the craftsman will have to overcome to produce the required finished products.

Forming elliptical curves

There are several methods of setting out and forming elliptical shapes. These range from a variety of geometrical methods with compasses, the trammel method to the complexities of the parabolic shapes favoured by the ancient Greeks. These are formed with a series of radiating lines from various positions to achieve a series of intersecting points which, when connected with each other, will form an elliptical curve. A thin flexible steel or plastic straight edge can be used to form the outline required. Whichever method is used to form the moulding, each one will require a different process and technique in its construction and application.

The multi-centred ellipse, three or five centred (Figure 5), will require a running mould and gig-stick to be used, and 'run off' from the different radius lengths. Each section must be cut with precision to the common normals for the curves. This will enable a perfect tangential joint to be produced when assembling the various sections to achieve the required shape.

Where a trammel method is to be used, a wooden trammel board (Figure 6) has to be constructed with accurately fitting sliding blocks. The running mould and gig-stick has two pivot plates fixed in position. When the board is secured to the background, the running mould is positioned on the pivot blocks, and the moulding can be 'run off'. It must be pointed out that running with the trammel will cause the moulding to become distorted width-wise in certain areas.

The parabolic ellipse is set out full size on the background, and the running rule line is plotted from the curve. The curved rule is fixed in position, and the running mould, a peg mould (Figure 7), on a flat background or a half-slippered three-legged mould on a curved background is run and guided completely by hand. A great deal of expertise is required when negotiating the changing actions of the hands and body movements compared with the rigid guides and pivots of the previous methods. At all times the metal profile must be at normal to the curve.

Fig. 7 Peg mould and curved rule

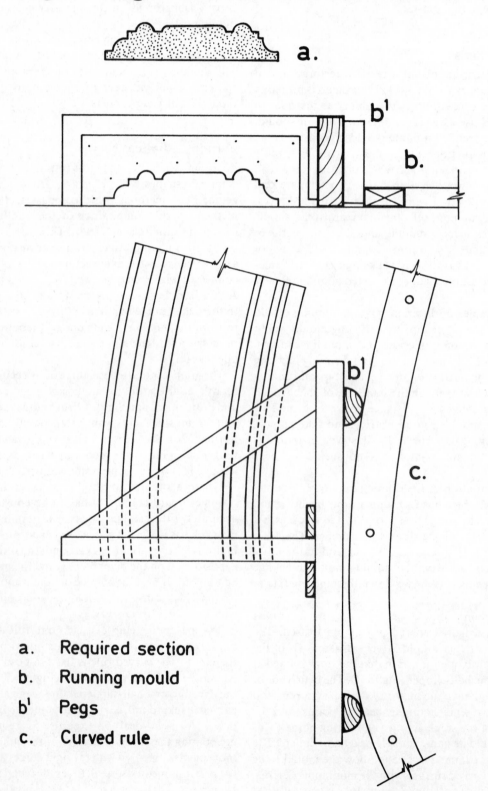

a.

b¹

b.

b¹

c.

a.   Required section
b.   Running mould
b¹   Pegs
c.   Curved rule

Squeezes

All preparation work for the restoration of unsound plasterwork must be completely thorough and accurate. Some of the methods used have been mentioned earlier in this chapter concerning loose and damaged areas.

When surveying moulded and enriched work, it should be well documented with measurements and sketches of the features, the types of enrichment noted together with their correct directional flow, i.e. running from right to left. This will ensure that the new model work is correctly set out and not back to front, as can easily happen.

To obtain all the essential dimensions, the use of certain tools and equipment will be necessary. These include a plumb-bob, centre bob and line, small and large squares, a spirit level, measuring rods or tapes and a straight edge. With these 'tools', the radii, diameters and rises can be calculated on domework and arches. On cornice work the depth and projection are measured. Panelled ceilings will have the sections recorded, together with the shapes, i.e. circular, interlacing square or lozenged, etc. When measuring columns and pilasters the entasis will have to be established. The diameters and widths of the base and necking sections are measured, together with the number, types of flute and fillet and any other relevant information. Where new moulded work has to be fitted to a curved background, its radius will have to be established geometrically or a template is accurately marked out to the curve.

The squeezes can now be taken and the necessary sections of enrichments carefully removed. All sections will be set out as full size drawings from which the working profiles will be produced. The running moulds for *in situ*, reverse work and model making work can be prepared and constructed with the necessary allowances made for the 'bed' areas where required.

The amount of enrichment to be removed from its *in situ* position will depend on firstly, the length of the repeat pattern and, secondly, the general condition of the original work. All sections that are removed will naturally be replaced with new work when refixing the new reproduction work.

It is a good policy to clean all distemper and paintwork off the enriched work as the original *in situ* work can always be restored to its former lines, shapes and details if the occasion arises. The new work will exactly match up with the original.

When cleaning paint from sections of enrichment, small items can be submerged in boiling water until the paint softens and begins to lift from the plaster. The sections are then removed for a further operation of cleaning. Using soft haired brushes and metal carving tools, the paintwork is brushed away with hot water, and carefully eased from the plaster features without scoring the original work.

On large areas of plasterwork the paintwork is soaked by brushing hot water over it or by using a steam kettle. This will cause the paint to soften up and it can then be cleaned.

In addition to the squeezes already mentioned here, there is the mechanical template former. This consists of thin strips of metal held in position by a clamp. To operate this tool one must open up the twin screws and press the strips against the moulding. Then, with the aid of a wooden peg, press the strip into the moulding. The shape will be recorded as the reverse, while the actual shape will be recorded at the opposite side of the template. The use of this instrument is invaluable for small sections of plain moulding without any undercut areas, for example architraves and panel mouldings.

In the main, squeezes are used to obtain a profile of a moulded section and positions of enrichments which may be contained within the sections.

Squeezes can also be used to form a reverse mould. This would be suitable for light relief work, i.e. strap-work. Obviously as plaster is used to form the squeeze, all undercut areas must be blocked out with clay before the squeeze is obtained, and carved out again on the cast.

The method of forming this type of squeeze is similar to casting from a mould in the fibrous plaster shop, but upside down. All areas of the ceiling not being treated should be covered with paper and taped up. A wall of clay is fixed around the required section or sections to provide a clean and neat perimeter to work to. The area to be used is now treated with a release agent; this is a very important operation and the work must be thorough, leaving a thin but even coating. All the reinforcing material is prepared, normally hessian canvas with 6 mm mesh. A large stout flat board is greased and the struts are cut to the required length. The quantity of plaster necessary to cover the area with a 'firsting' or a first coat of plaster is gauged up. The 'seconds' or second coat of plaster should be soaked until required.

The method of casting the squeeze is as follows: with a plasterer's splash brush, brush a thin layer of 'firstings' thoroughly over the entire area, making sure all the moulding has been covered evenly and without any misses. The next operation is to splash a layer of plaster over the same area to build up a reasonable thickness. This stage of the operation is by far the dirtiest as it involves holding the splash brush full of plaster in one hand and flicking it *upwards* on to the ceiling. The operatives generally cover their head, arms and bodies with plastic sheeting or paper bags for added protection.

The next stage is to gauge or mix the 'seconds' and brush and splash a layer on to the previously prepared greased board, while for reinforcement soak the canvas strips in plaster and lay opened out on the board. Add the plaster evenly over the canvas and gradually build up to the required thickness as the plaster thickens and becomes 'cheesy' (the process of setting). Before the 'firstings' sets, the board covered with plaster and canvas is offered up to the 'firstings' and pressed on to it. It is held in position by the wooden struts until the plaster sets.

The size of the 'cast squeeze' will depend on, firstly, the area that can be safely managed by the craftsmen with the weight of the plaster and supporting board and, secondly, the length and area of a repeat section. It is always a good policy to have at least two people to perform this operation. If more than one squeeze is to be taken to form a complete section, then the ceiling must be marked out, and the 'finished casts' can be cut to the marks to achieve an exact copy of the original.

The 'cast squeeze' is only removed when the firsting and seconds have completely set. The removal operation must be performed with care, by taking the weight of the board and carefully removing the supporting struts. At this time, the whole squeeze will want to fall down. Therefore, it must be gradually eased away from the ceiling to avoid the possibility of damaging the original work.

The cast squeeze can now be prepared and treated for casting as a normal reverse mould. All protective covering on the ceiling can be removed, the grease release agent wiped off with dry canvas and the ceiling cleaned off with methylated spirits.

When taking squeezes of this nature it is important that the seconds be applied to the firstings before it sets to achieve perfect adhesion with each other. Failure to do so could result in the face work 'cockling' which is a bumpy and uneven finish. Cleaning up the face work with this fault is often more time-consuming than retaking the whole squeeze again.

Large squeezes can also be used to help to straighten ceilings that have sagged away from the timber joists. The main concern with this operation is the protection of the enriched areas. These sections can be protected by thick sheets of expanded polystyrene acting as the main padding material. The gaps between the flat ceiling and the face of the enrichments can also be packed with polystyrene and timber to give added support. Plaster backs to the padding can be used to give extra rigidity if necessary.

The basic method used to straighten up the old ceiling is to strut rigid boards and padding against the plasterwork, and gradually lever or, alternatively, use folding wedges to raise the board with the struts until the ceiling is back in its original position.

Before the straightening procedure can commence the back of the ceiling must be thoroughly cleaned free of all rubble, broken plaster, dust, soot and, on occasions, birds' nests. Where the lathing has rotted it must be removed, together with all loose work under the joists. A dust pan and brush can be used for the large pieces of rubble, and an industrial vacuum cleaner for the finishing touches. Once the back has been cleaned the ceiling can be carefully jacked back into position.

To fix and secure the ceiling back into its original position the back of the ceiling is treated with a sealer and bonding agent. A PVA solution is an ideal material, and this is liberally brushed over the back. Originally, shellac or paint was used to help eliminate the suction and prevent the new plaster back staining the old paintwork. The back of the ceiling and the supports are cast over with plaster gauged up in size water to retard its setting time, then covered by two layers of hessian canvas. Laths can be incorporated in the 'back' on-edge to gain additional extra strength. Where, because of re-flooring, the joists cannot be cast over, extra noggin pieces are fixed in between them and large canvas laps are soaked in plaster and draped over the noggins, and pressed and brushed on to the ceiling's back.

With the completion of treatment to the ceiling the task of dismantling the support work on the underside can begin. This work must be carefully executed to avoid possible damage to the enrichments and mouldings. The ceiling should be thoroughly inspected and any cracks and repair work completed.

Before an operation of this type is attempted, the scaffolding should be made rigid to prevent the support work from vertical movement. It is recommended that wherever possible the floor should be used for this purpose.

Removal of ceilings for renovation

When circumstances dictate that a ceiling has to be removed, the reasons being either that the original timber support work has seriously deteriorated or the existing site is scheduled for redevelopment, the whole of the plasterwork must be encased in a cocoon of plaster, canvas, padding and supporting boards (as described before), and removed, stored and refixed when required.

A very good example of this type of work is the one illustrated in Plate 1, 'The Dutch House' in Chester. The ceiling is approximately 200 years old, and the three enriched centre bays were taken down by removing the floorboards and all the debris on top of the ceiling, then after carefully supporting the ceiling from below, the

wooden lathing was removed. At this stage the joists were strengthened by screwing lengths of timber battening across them at 300 mm intervals. This gave added support when the ceiling, together with sections of the joists, were removed in panels of approximately 1 m², and transported back to the fibrous workshop in London.

In the workshop the delicate task of removing the timber work and cleaning the ceiling proceeded. The back was reinforced with class A plaster, canvas and timber reinforcing. New beam cases and cornices were produced to match the existing work. The painstaking job of removing the countless layers of distemper and paint from the moulding enrichments was carried out with great skill. Where the original embellishments were missing, PVC moulds were obtained from similar matching areas, and casts were reproduced and fitted into the defective area and made good to the ceiling until the whole work was once again a complete entity.

When the task of preparing and renewing the timber joists had been completed on-site, the final stage of refixing the plasterwork ceiling back in position took place. The ceiling and beam case positions were set out with chalk lines and refixed with galvanized wire hangers and secured in position with plaster wads. All joints and mitres were then 'stopped in' or made good.

The new ceiling is now evidence of what can be achieved when faced with the problems of preserving early and historic plasterwork.

(We are grateful to Thomas and Wilson Ltd., London, for the photograph and information on the "Dutch House".)

4 Repairs to internal enriched moulded work *in situ*

This work can vary from complete renewal of all plastering right back to the background, down to just small repairs to damaged enrichment. Where the first condition exists the treatment of the background and the application of subsequent coats of plaster will be as for repairs to internal plain surfacing. The mouldings may be run or planted on to the new finished surface. A metal profile should be cut as described in the section on preparatory work and the running mould 'horsed up'. Where enrichment exists beds will be run and the enrichment cast from moulds and planted into the beds. The decision as to whether or not the moulding should be run in position or run down on a board and planted will depend on site conditions, but this decision need not be affected by the specification wording '*in situ*'. Many of the old panelled plaster ceilings and walls were run down, the back wall keyed and the moulding 'planted', in other words stuck in position with plaster or nailed.

Another old method used to form enriched panel ceilings and strapwork was to cast the panels solid, very often with part of the backing. A section of the ceiling was run down and completed on a board and a solid gypsum plaster mould made from this. The mould face was sealed and treated with a fat or oil before each cast. A plaster/lime mix was then poured into the mould and the mould wedged into position so that its back contacted and adhered to the prepared background. When the mixture set the mould was eased away leaving the cast in position. The operation was repeated many times until the entire ceiling was completed. All joints and irregularities were then cleaned and stopped and any undercut section carved by hand.

This method may still be used today in the restoration of such ceilings or walls. The mould may be cast in position on part of the ceiling that is sound. Alternatively, an original may be built up on the bench either from newly run work or from parts of the damaged ceiling that have fallen or have been removed. Two matters to be considered prior to casting the mould in position are, firstly, is there any undercut on the moulding? If there is this will prevent the mould from being released or, worse still, may cause even greater damage to the ceiling. Secondly, the making of a reverse plaster mould in position may well prove to be a dirty job, in so far as it is awkward to cast upside down and much splashing may result.

The normal procedure is to position boundary walls of wood or clay, and then treat the entire surface with grease. The existing paintwork should act as a sealant. The firstings are gauged much thicker than is usual and should be well sized. A combination of brushing and trowelling is probably the best method of application, but whichever way is used the plaster must be well worked in to all existing members. A backing piece of solid wood is applied before the firstings have set. This is done by heaping plaster on to the surface of a piece of specially prepared rigid blockboard and levelling to the required thickness. It is then pushed into the firstings on the ceiling and strutted in position. This method can only be used on low relief work and, where a similar situation exists on high relief, the mould can be made using more usual casting techniques. Thick, well sized firstings are applied and these are reinforced by the application of battens and canvas and the whole mould is then well strutted from the floor or scaffold.

Another method used to make a reverse mould of antique plaster is to run lengths of moulding on a scaffold board, using clay as a medium instead of plaster. Allow the clay to part dry; as it does so it will go out of shape and twist. Then cast a solid plaster mould over the clay. From this mould plaster casts can be obtained. These are cut into the required shapes and sizes and made into a model panel. From this another mould is obtained and the casts from this will appear as old freehand plastering as the twists and shakes that took place in the drying clay are repeated in the plaster casts.

Plaster columns and pilasters

Another area where a squeeze or cast *in situ* mould may be of considerable use is in the repair or even complete restoration of fluted columns or pilasters. The method can only be used where the fluting is shallow; deep fluting will be too undercut other than for single casts, or on pilasters. Select an area of the damaged column (or an undamaged column) and with clay check for 'draw'. This means push in a clay squeeze on to a chalked background to see how many flutes will draw without being affected by undercut. Two or three very shallow flutes will probably be the maximum. Having ascertained the number, produce several plaster squeezes about 50 mm wide and 50 mm thick. Set out the column size on the floor or board and lay the reverse squeezes in position. From this, collars can be prepared to use as a guide for the repairs to the old columns. At least three collars will be required; one at maximum height where the diminished column is at its smallest; a second or central collar to assist in the formation of the entasis; and a base collar to bring the column out to its fullest size at base level. Part or whole columns can be ruled into these collars using prepared entasis rules; one rule for the backing coats; one for fillet rim size; and a sharp featheredge rule for cutting the flutes. The method is really only suitable for the largest of columns so that once the well ruled finish plaster has hardened to a very good shape, both for fluting and fillets, a smooth finish can be obtained using small tools and purpose-made trowels, plasterers' busk and, as on one site visited recently, wet and dry glass paper.

Where major repairs are necessary or the columns are fairly small it is suggested that the fluting is run down on a board using the diminished mould method. The fluting may then be planted in position and the joints stopped in. In both cases it may be necessary to produce a small individual mould that can be used to assist in the formation of the flute ends.

A refinement used recently included the casting of a complete flute mould from an existing column. This was then used to press flutes from the collars or, as in one case, form existing work. Once again, the finishing had to be by purpose-made hand tools. Wooden dowling, the size and shape of the fluting tightly covered by wet and dry glass paper, was used in much the same way as a wooden float in the formation of external cement columns.

Where damage has occurred to either capital or base to a column or pilaster, a similar method may be necessary. Should the damage be anything larger than that which can be hand-carved, small reverse moulds cast in position may be the answer. Another possibility is the making up of a complete model capital or base from fragments or pieces saved from damaged areas. This can then be used for moulding. Once again the *in situ* specification need cause no fears here as in most cases the original was probably part run, part planted.

A major concern today is the materials. Many of the old columns were formed in Keene's cement which is, generally speaking, out of favour today. It may be possible to get hold of some purpose-made anhydrous plaster, but in many instances this is unlikely. Even the modern class C plaster has little in common with its predecessor. So what do we use? One reason for Keene's being used for columns and pilasters was its hardness, and it was also easy to use. A suggestion today is to use either class B wall finish gypsum plaster or, again as seen recently, class A plaster heavily retarded with size. This gives time for working and also provides the hardness. However, there is a snag since it expands drastically on setting. A little lime putty will cut down on this and it also reduces the hardness. A well keyed backing is essential and when using class A plaster take one or two precautions. Either use a well formed Portland cement/ sand backing, cut down on the thickness of the plaster or add the plaster in thinnish coats, keying well every time. An alternative backing coat could be class A plaster/sharp sand gauged half and half.

A typical example of how the expansion of both class A and class B gypsum plaster can affect the final solution was shown recently on a restoration site. Here the old lime plaster finishing coat had parted company with its backing coat. After complete removal of the finishing only, the backing was brushed dry and then dampened. To this a coat of class B finish was applied. Within a short time it had lifted free from the old backing coat, pulling a fine layer of the lime and sand with it. A percentage of lime and a surface treatment to the backing coat produced a satisfactory answer the second time around.

Enriched solid run cornices (Figure 8)

Hand carved repair work will require great skill and a wide assortment of plasterers' small tools. The materials used should commence with a good PVA surface sealer, class A gypsum plaster and good lime putty.

All loose particles of the old work must be removed. The clean surface should then be well scored and finally treated with the sealer. The enrichment is best built out rather gradually, and where possible lines should be worked in first. By this we mean the straight run members should be ruled in right across the damaged area. To do this one may use a metal joint rule, and these are available in lengths that vary from about 50 mm up to 600 mm, a good average size being between 300–450 mm. These must be used with skill and with two techniques; firstly, as with a stroking action when the material is still pliable; secondly, with a cutting action when the plaster is hard. Enrichment may be hand-carved or produced from small individual clay or plasticine squeezes.

Where larger lengths of enriched cornice have been damaged and the repairs must be in solid plastering as opposed to fibrous plastering, the answer is to run all continuous members. Included on the metal profile must be beds for the enrichment. Where the enrichment is sufficiently heavy, as in the case of egg and dart, plain right-angled beds will be sufficient to take the casts from a normal mould. Where the enrichment is finer, as in the case of a frieze ornament, quilloche or fret, it will be better to cut the bed to a depth of something like 5 mm extra and then cast this extra thickness so as to form a base on the casts. Very often the lightest of frieze moulds are made from composition. This material dates back to late 1700s and is a mixture of Scotch glue and ground resin (see Chapter 7). It was used to form ornamental picture and mirror frames and to provide very fine ornament for decorative cornices. When fixing composition the casts were rendered slightly pliable by holding them over steam. Then they were very gently tacked using fine panel pins where they were hardly visible. The steam also made the back of the casts slightly tacky; this formed a self-made adhesive. Composition should never be nailed up really cold as it

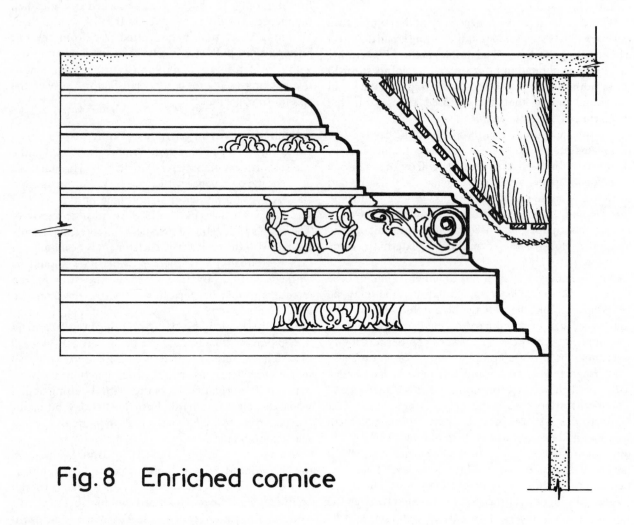

Fig. 8   Enriched cornice

will probably split and splinter. Unfortunately, this material has now been superseded by the ready-made plastic casts obtainable from many DIY shops!

To return to the running operation, as in all plastering, the background must be sound and joints between new and old work cut square, keyed and sealed. A rule is nailed to the wall on which the mould slipper will rest and the front edge of the slipper is kept away from the wall surface by a rabbit or rebate. The position of the rule is determined by the jointing of old and new work and great care should be taken over the placement. Brackets may be needed to save both weight and material; to these wood or metal lathing may be fixed. Work on these must consist of a render coat which will contain a fibrous material and be either gypsum plaster gauged coarse stuff or gypsum plaster and sand, in both

cases from half and half to two parts coarse stuff/sand to one part class A plaster. A muffle run of a similar mix to a well keyed core that will leave an approximate finish thickness of 3–4 mm would be the next operation. This should be lightly keyed ready to receive the finish of either half and half class A gypsum plaster and lime putty or up to two parts lime putty. The mix may be left to the man on the site and points to remember will vary from the expansion problem caused by using neat plaster to the softness of the cornice caused by using too weak a mix. Jointing and the formation of mitres is far better in both accuracy and finish when the cornice is hard. The joint rule no matter how gently and expertly used will frequently cause slight damage to the soft moulding. Mitres should be worked in the same way as for jointing. Start from the top and form one or two members at a time. Check for intersection and also for the way the ornament is required to work out in the mitres.

The jointing of enrichment at mitres can be a major problem. The usual method when planning *in situ* is to get all mitres to match. This may be done by stretching or shrinking the pliable plastic moulds or, should the moulds be of plaster or wax, stretching or shrinking the enrichment. To do this one would start to lose or gain measurement at a distance from the mitre that would not attract attention. The actual distance would be measured accurately and the plaster casts would be cut with a fine toothed saw at points where repairs would be easily carried out. For shrinking, one would remove, say, 2 mm for several eggs in egg and dart, and for stretching, one would open the gaps to lengthen by a similar distance. On some sites this would be unnecessary as the mitres would be blotted out by use of a mitre leaf or some similar purpose-made ornament fitting both internal and external mitres.

The casting and planting of lines of enrichment *in situ* is an exacting task. All casts must be accurately struck off at the back. This will ensure a perfect seating in the bed. The end will be cast to repeat or follow on and both the bedding up and the jointing will need the utmost care and attention to obtain straight lines of enrichment. Some craftsmen will use a line, rather like a bricklayer when bedding. Others prefer to handle a rule, lining in from the ornament that has been bedded previously. The eye is also essential, and here we suggest a good long look from as many angles as possible, including ground level when one is working on a scaffold.

Suction from a dry or drying backing can cause problems, yet a little is necessary when planting in the horizontal. Dampening may suffice or a weak mix of PVA and water. A small amount of this adhesive may also be added to the water before mixing the plaster to improve adhesive qualities.

Should old enrichment have to be removed from the original cornices, it will have been fastened by one of several traditional methods. Apart from plaster or plaster and lime, a mixture of lime and size water was used and, of course, the old favourite, burnt shellac. Many older craftsmen did not like the latter method as it could cause staining should it spread, but it was probably the best when used correctly, though it would need supports in the initial stages as it slipped until it hardened.

Old modillions were often spiked in position, held up by large cut nails. These were given a coat of shellac to prevent rusting, then driven through drilled holes in the solid casts and punched below the surface. As the cornices of that age were good thick solid run mouldings

the nails would hold, in fact, in lots of cases have until today. The reason for having to know these fixing methods is that quite frequently one may have to remove a fixed cast so that it can become a model from which a mould can be obtained. As referred to in Chapter 1 on the historical backgound, this type of moulding and casting can be quite legitimately listed under the heading of solid plastering.

The running and planting method does not apply to cornice work only. Quite often an enriched moulding will appear in the form of pediments, architraves, archivolts and dado moulds. Where damage or decay is great, running is always better than forming. In a book such as this we would need many more pages to describe the various types of running mould which a plasterer would have to make to cope with every type of restoration. Having dealt with a good straight run and having spelt out the basics for the making of a running mould, all it needs is a study of the problem to see how the running should be done and where the rule needs to be placed.

What may be more important is a study of the background and backing coats. What materials have been used? Do they form a sound base on which to build the new mouldings? Is it important to match up in material specification? Architraves, plinths and skirtings were frequently run in solid, using a coarse Keene's and sand backing with a fine Keene's finish. What can one use today that will reproduce the hardness and durability of Keene's? Again, the recommendation will be class A gypsum plaster with plenty of size added to the mixing water. However, before putting this into practice one should have confidence that the people involved have the necessary skill, technique and knowledge of material behaviour to cope. This would ensure that the gradual build-up system would be used. Thin coat application of such materials would make certain that the expansion that takes place with the setting of a class A gypsum plaster would spread over a period of time and not take place all at once. There is, of course, no reason why much of the moulding coming under discussion cannot be run down and then planted. Because of the thickness and solidity of a fully run section it will have greater durability than, say, ordinary fibrous plaster, though this can be both hardened and strengthened tremendously when one knows just what additional strength is required.

Another problem is what backing plaster to apply when the removal of moulded features has destroyed the original backing coats? It is very often more convenient to both specify and apply the modern premixed lightweight plasters as these can result in the backing and finishing being carried out in one day. However, they do not form the ideal backing for strongly gauged gypsum plaster/lime putty mouldings. These have been known to pull away as the setting action of the run plaster reaches its climax. The answer on one site, where the newly run cornice was of a fairly plain design, was to do all the work in premixed lightweight plasters, including the running. This does happen on some new building sites so it would appear that it could become an accepted practice.

The application of OPC, lime and sand backing coats is a more traditional method of tackling the problem, and it has proved successful. There is, of course, the time lag between the application of coats and the drying out time. To solve the first of these problems on normal backgrounds, the use of the retarded hemihydrate class B browning plaster mixed with sand is again a well proven method. Here one should check on the suitability of the plaster to the background, but in reality it is only what plasterers were doing many years ago, the difference being that before the introduction of retarded plasters one had to do it for oneself. The addition of glue size water and lime provided the answer. One note of caution here: the mixing of a class A gypsum plaster to a normal building sand can cause an acceleration of set due to the impurities being present in the sand.

Running in solid plaster using screeds

Some readers might wonder why we did not mention this in the preparatory work chapter. The main reason is that whenever working on restoration work a rebate or rabbit has always seemed the best method to use. By using a good thick running rule, say, 50 mm by 25 mm, with a correctly fixed rabbit, no screed has been necessary. However, it has been suggested that as there are times when a running screed is more convenient to use than a rabbit, a short commentary on this subject should be included.

The running mould should be offered up into position at the corners of the room on all walls. Marks should be made at nib and slipper positions. From these marks chalk lines are struck so that two nice clean lines run entirely around the room, one on the wall at slipper depth, one on the ceiling at nib projection.

Lime putty and plaster is mixed at the ratio of equal proportions and applied to both wall and ceiling in a narrow band of some 60–70 mm straddling the chalk lines. The screeds are then ruled flat using a featheredge rule worked at right angles to the screeds. Once these have been ruled flat, a wooden float, preferably a crossgrain, should be laid flat on the screeds and rubbed along the entire length leaving a good 'closed in' surface. The mould is held in position again, wall and ceiling screed surface re-marked, and new chalk lines struck. To the wall line the rule is fixed while the ceiling can be used as a guide.

Points to remember: screeds should be no thicker than the normal finishing coat, say, 2–4 mm; they should never exceed 70 or 75 mm in width, in fact 50–60 mm is even better; they must be ruled absolutely flat, and never finished by laying trowel, always a flat wooden float.

These screeds eliminate the necessity for a rabbit or rebate and where the moulding is something other than a cornice, substitute the ceiling screed with a nib screed.

Starting from the uppermost or outer member of the run moulding, apply just sufficient gypsum plaster and lime putty, both in depth and thickness, to form the complete length of one member. Using either a plasterers' metal smalltool or a small gauging trowel, build out so as to form a really good shape of the required member. Holding a joint rule in two hands so that the cutting or bevel edge runs parallel to the straight members, move to the top or outer member. The length of the joint rule should be sufficient to bear on the existing work at both ends of the damaged area. Draw the joint rule away from all external arrises in a cutting fashion and move gently but firmly into the internal angles of the moulding. Keep the tool clean and add additional plaster where necessary. When this member has a shape that matches the existing one perfectly, move on to the next section and repeat the operation. Continue to repeat the operation until the cornice or moulding section has been completed. A perfect finish can be obtained by lightly dampening the work and applying a softer or wetter mix of gypsum plaster and lime putty over the wet area. The joint rule is then used flatter so that the mix is worked into the face. The result should be a smooth clean surface to the repaired section. This operation needs plenty of practice in all shapes of moulding and in all the various mixes. The more gypsum plaster or the stronger and harder surface, the more upright the joint rule. It should be kept almost at right angles to the work and the edge used to cut. The softer or weaker the final set the smaller the angle between joint rule and surface. Even these mixes will harden and any surplus plaster will be removed again by the cutting action. Only practice and experience can really guide one's hand at such times. Again, the background preparation must be stressed. All old weak dusty work must be removed and the remaining surface must be scored and keyed.

Restoration work on *in situ* mouldings to a curved background

Wherever possible the work should run in position; however, there are times when it may be more convenient to prepare a curved background on the floor

Fig. 9   Run loose piece reverse mould

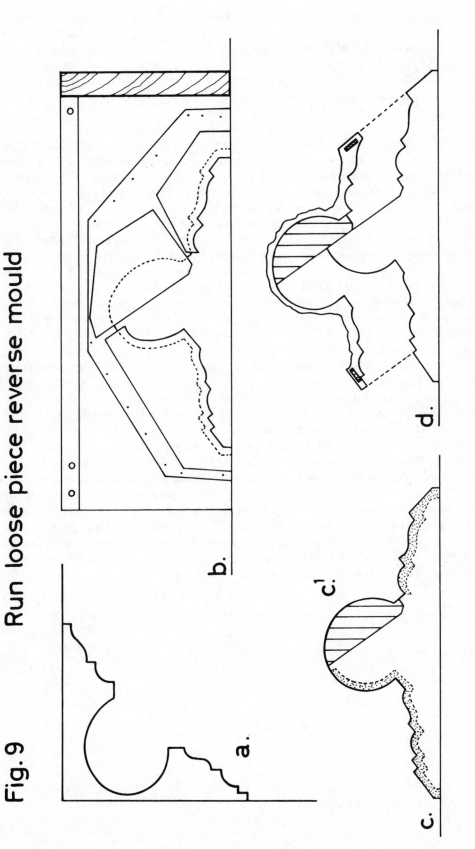

a. Section of cornice
b. Running mould with bed and muffle plates
c. Reverse mould and run loose piece (c¹)
d. Cast and loose being removed

or scaffold, run all mouldings on this background and then plant them in position. In both instances, provided the curve is a regular one, the running mould slipper must be shaped to the curve. The process of running will be the same as for straight mouldings. One additional difficulty will be encountered – that of fixing rules to a curved background. This may be overcome by either using thin rules with just enough thickness to take the slipper, or, alternatively, several thin rules, nailed one on top of the other, a method frequently used by plasterers. A slightly thicker rule with regular half depth vertical saw cuts on the back surface is another method, but this may only be used when running on lime putty and plaster screeds behind the rules. The saw cuts may produce a slightly irregular front rule face and this would prevent one from using the curved work alternative to a rabbit, a peg mould (see Figure 7).

Where the curve is other than purely circular, a half-slippered three peg mould is usually used. 'Half-slippered' or 'bare-faced' mean that the profile and stock are mounted at the front of the slipper rather than in the centre. The slipper is then cut to a convenient length and two pegs or screws are driven into the underside of the slipper in such a position as to prevent the inner slipper face from making contact with the wall, thus performing exactly the same function as a rabbit or rebate. This is why the front face of the running rule must be free from irregularities. It may also be better for the inner slipper face to be cut back, leaving two pegs free to perform correctly, the third peg being the mould nib.

This operation can be very difficult where curves are exaggerated or even changing and a certain amount of practice may be required to produce a satisfactory finish. Many plasterers will prefer to run the mouldings down on the background that has been prepared from a series of squeezes that will produce a perfect facsimile of the wall or ceiling curves. Where the mouldings contain enrichment this method is again used, the flexible reverse moulds being laid on a temporary background, the reverse of the curved surface of the finished work.

Handforming

One of the biggest problems when it comes to repair work to any of the moulded features is adhesion. Behind the relatively hard surfaces on many of these features a soft friable backing will be found. (It is this factor which gave birth to the idea that the hard surface was obtained by tooling.) To apply a strong hard gypsum plaster directly to this will cause two major problems. The first is that as the plaster sets it expands. This will cause the freshly applied plaster to pull away from the old work. The second problem is one of practicability. Due to the hardness of the new plaster it will have to be cut or carved rather than being tooled. This will require pressure being applied to form matching lines with the existing work. When this is done damage is frequently caused to the old work. Provided the work is out of reach, a 1:3 or 4 gypsum plaster/lime putty mix will cut this problem out. The material may be applied by plasterers' smalltool and roughly shaped to form a good facsimile of the feature required. A final light carving by sharp carving tools will give the perfect finish. The old backing must be well scored, and sealed to control suction and to prevent the spread of water.

With all handforming, whether it is repair work or forming mitres and joints to new work, the method must be to apply little at a time and form as good a shape as possible with the wet plaster. In many ways it is best to practice this skill by carrying out repairs to straight run mouldings or cornices before attempting the completely freehand modelling.

5 Repairs and replacement of mouldings in fibrous plaster

In this chapter we will deal with fibrous plasterwork. As will be seen, solid and fibrous work may overlap, but in certain circumstances specialist skills and treatment in either area will be needed. A good example of this work would be the need to preserve a highly enriched cornice, while renewing a badly damaged main ceiling area. The method of work is to assess the extent of the damage and support the cornice with padding material, boards and struts from the floor if possible or the scaffolding. A sharp saw is used to cut the plaster along the ceiling line close to the cornice, carefully removing a section of the ceiling and exposing the background. The area above and slightly behind the cornice is cleaned out to form a recess. This area can now be treated (to prevent any excessive suction) and canvas and plaster wads used to bond the upper side of the cornice to the existing background.

This operation is repeated until the whole cornice has been inspected and 'refixed'.

The main ceiling area can now be carefully removed and replastered, as described in Chapter 2.

When reproducing damaged moulded work in fibrous plaster two methods can be employed. The first method involves the construction of a reverse running mould (Figure 1), and forming a one-piece reverse mould for casting work without any undercut features. The type of reverse mould used to produce undercut work is a 'run loose piece' mould, where the loose-piece section together with the finished cast is removed from the mould. The loose-piece is carefully removed from the cast, and replaced in the mould ready for the casting process to commence again (see Figure 9).

The second method of reproducing the moulding known as 'run-cast' also involves the construction of a running mould. This time, it will be used to run the required section, together with the canvas and lath reinforcing materials. Using this method a film of plaster is laid on the bench and covered with a strip of canvas. The reinforcing laths are positioned on the canvas and covered with a second layer of canvas. The running mould is then drawn along the rule over the canvas, and checked to see that the canvas does not foul the template line. Plaster is gradually built-up and run off with the running mould until the required finish is achieved. The finished item will be, in effect, a solid cast.

Where the moulding has some depth to it a core of clay, sand, brick etc., covered with wet newspaper or plaster is formed. The run-cast is now formed over the core at a reasonable thickness and weight (Figure 10).

All methods have their own advantages. The first method would be used for large sections of moulding or where numerous casts are required. The second method can be used where the amount needed is minor, a 'one

off' situation. It can also be used on-site, as in running down mouldings for breaks.

Prior to fixing the fibrous casts, all fixing points are established and clearly marked. The setting out of the new work is carefully measured and marked out with a chalk-line. This will match up and blend in with the existing work. The casts can now be measured and the mitres and lengths cut to size. When fixing to 'solid' backgrounds, rustless nails or screws are used and slightly countersunk. Before 'stopping-in', all joints and mitres are adjusted and checked for alignment. The finished work should be indistinguishable from the original with the exception of the colour of the new plaster.

Where the moulding contains enrichments, the procedure for replacement is as for the two methods mentioned earlier, with a provision for a recess section being made in the working profile to receive the separately cast sections of enrichments. After the casts have been fixed on-site then reproduction of mouldings and enriched features will be carried out as detailed in Chapter 3 under *squeezes*.

Repairs to existing fibrous work

As fibrous plasterwork has been in existence for over a hundred years, it is possible that the older work will be in need of restoration or minor repairs, normally the result of new construction work, or structural repairs. Once again a thorough survey is made to assess the amount of work to be renewed or repaired. All squeezes, measurements and enrichments are noted for the reproduction work and the moulds and casts can be produced for refixing.

To remove the defective fibrous work, establish the full extent of the damaged area, and clearly mark out the lines to cut to. Wherever possible keep all the lines straight and square as this procedure will help when setting out the new model work, which will in turn provide the correct positions for the reinforcing and fixing timbers in the casts.

In certain situations the cast has to be cut to fit an irregular shape. Sometimes fixing laths are removed. These laths can be replaced by wadding new timber pieces in position on the back of the cast where they will perform a double function. Firstly, to provide fixing areas and, secondly, to strengthen the edges. All preparation is done before the fixing procedure can commence.

Removal of existing fibrous work

To remove the existing damaged fibrous plaster, mark out the extent of the area concerned and with a sharp hand-saw cut through the plaster around the outline.

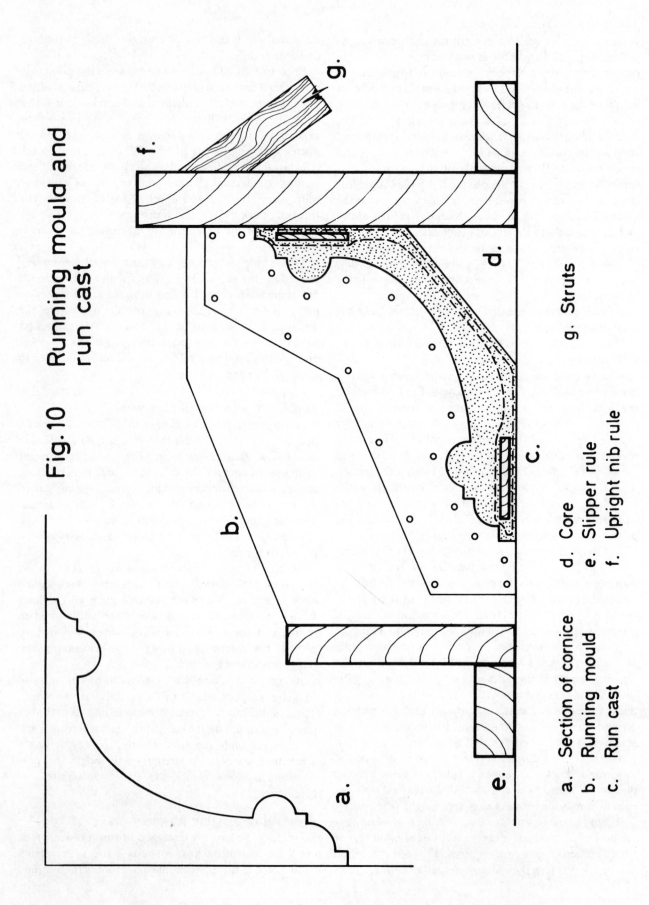

Fig.10 Running mould and run cast

a. Section of cornice
b. Running mould
c. Run cast
d. Core
e. Slipper rule
f. Upright nib rule
g. Struts

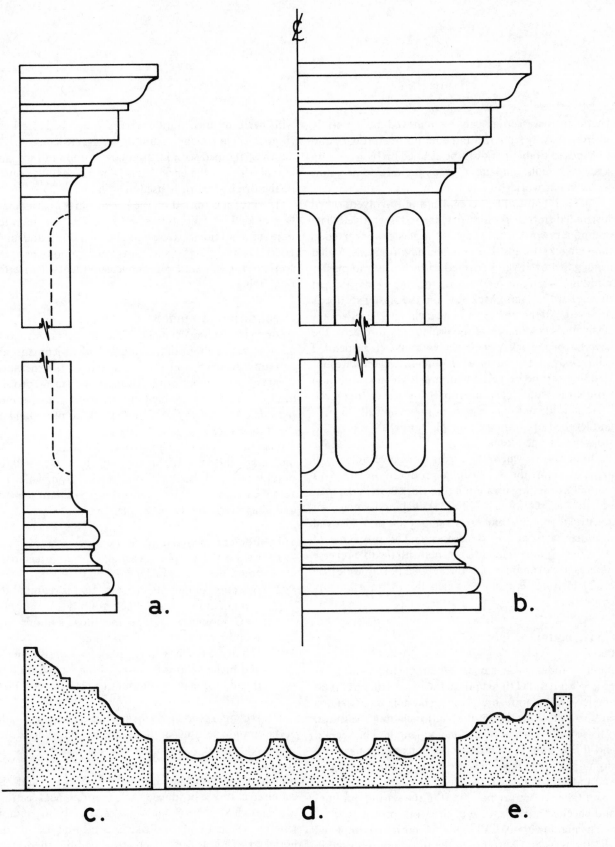

Fig.11   Plain moulded pilaster

a. Side elevation   c. Section through capital
b. Front elevation   d.   "   "   shaft
                          e.   "   "   base

The defective section can be removed by carefully levering it away from the timber joints or studwork and all exposed timberwork can be cleaned up by removing screws or nails, making it ready to receive the new replacement work.

There is an added complication involved when suspended fibrous plasterwork has to be removed. The preliminary work is the same as for plasterwork fixed to timber backgrounds. The casts will have been suspended using galvanized wires covered with canvas and plaster wadding. To remove these fixings the wads are cut through with a sharp hack-saw and the plaster section is removed. All the timber and metal channel formwork is cleaned of the remains of the wads ready to receive the new fibrous work. When access above a suspended ceiling is available, all the work of removing the wire and wadding can be executed with much greater ease than from large hand holes cut from below the ceiling level.

All new fibrous plasterwork must be carefully lined in and levelled up to the existing plaster before fixing and stopping can be attempted.

On occasions where the repair work is of only small areas or items, the work can be produced on-site. This will involve setting up a miniature workshop in the area or on the scaffolding. Most skilled craftsmen can construct running moulds from reverse moulds and produce casts on-site if necessary. The problems of reproducing undercut enrichments with flexible reverse moulds are overcome with the aid of a portable electric PVC melting container which is thermostatically controlled.

Construction of models
Plain
Plain moulded work is relatively simple to produce, for example a parallel fluted pilaster with a moulded capital and base will require three running moulds. The first one will be a cross-section of the shaft including the flutes. This section is 'run-off' and cut to length. The second and third running moulds are sections of the base and capital sections, these are also run off and the lengths and mitres are also cut to size.

All the sections are now fixed to the setting out lines and checked as each stage of the work proceeds.

The making good of all joints and mitres is completed and the tops and bottoms of the flutes are returned in themselves to semicircular or elliptical ends. These will resemble miniature niches or alcoves (Figure 11). From this model a reverse mould is cast.

Enriched
To produce an enriched model is a more exacting task than the work mentioned above. The working profiles will need to incorporate recesses or 'bed sections' (Figure 12) in which to plant down the enrichment. The depth of the bed section will depend upon the size and complexities of the enrichment, and normally a section of the original work is used as a guide.

The model is run off on the bench and the enrichment is moulded in PVC (see *flood moulds*). The required number of sections are cast and bedded down and made good. During this last stage it is important to check the sections for line and repeat measurements before the final fixing.

Preparation of models
Prior to the commencement of any model construction all squeezes, sections of mouldings and enrichments are carefully checked and reconstructed to the measurements of the original work. The necessary metal profiles are produced and horsed up to form the 'running moulds'. At this stage, two main methods of making up the 'models' can be used.

The first method is to produce a complete model including all the enrichments. Each model will be moulded (to achieve the reverse section from which the actual casts will be taken), according to its requirements and characteristics, for example:

1   For enriched flat panel type sections a flood mould of PVC plus a cast plaster reinforced back could be used.
2   A section of enriched cornice that is required for straight and curved backgrounds. A run case PVC mould would be the most suitable and economical method of moulding.
3   Where ornate brackets, trusses or console blocks and niche heads are required the work would be treated for clay case moulding to produce a PVC mould.

The second method is to form a plaster reverse mould of the straight sections of moulding, i.e. the fillets, cyma rectas etc., and include all the necessary 'beds' or recesses to receive the enrichment. The mould is prepared with shellac and a release agent and the required casts are produced. All the enrichment sections are moulded in PVC and cast separately in suitable lengths. The main plaster casts are fixed on site and the enriched sections are fixed by bedding them into position in the same manner as the original work was many years ago. This method is suitable for repairing small areas of work as it reduces the obvious cost involved in the other methods mentioned.

Flood moulds (using PVC)
We thought at this point we ought to mention in greater

Fig.12   Exploded view – an enriched cornice model, run core and case

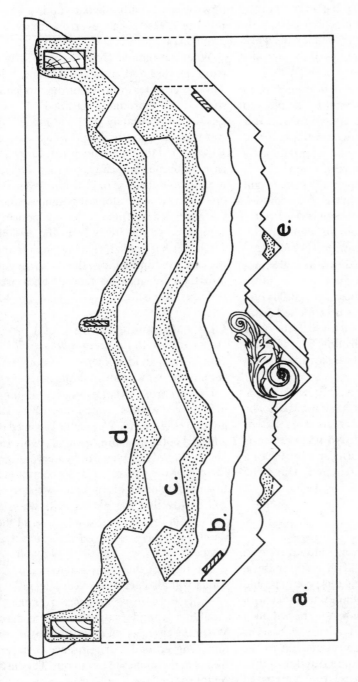

a.   Plaster model
b.   Wet paper
c   Run plaster core
d.   Plaster case
e.   Bed section and enrichment

detail the preparation and pouring of a flood mould with a polyvinyl chloride (PVC) compound.

PVC can be safely used on models of plaster, clay, stone, metal and plasticine. With the more porous materials like plaster and stone the models are best kept moist. Sometimes it may be necessary to soak the work in water. All surface water is removed before the pouring commences.

The method of producing the flood mould is as follows: the section of enrichment is cut to the pick-up lengths and, if required, cleaned of old paintwork. It is then bedded on to a moulding ground and all joints and the edges are made good. At a distance of approximately 40–50 mm from the model a wall of clay, wood or sheet metal is fixed in position around the model. Its height must be greater than the highest part of the model. Should a plaster back be required, for example when working in the circular positions, the walls are slightly tilted inwards to allow the back to be drawn off with ease.

The PVC compound is melted down in a thermostatically controlled electric tank. The size of tanks range from a portable 5 litre size to a 100 litre commercial size. When the PVC has been melted down it is poured from one end of the model towards the other end with the pouring kept behind the flow line. This will help to eliminate seams and air bubbles forming on the finished mould surface.

Care must be taken to ensure that the back of the flood mould is regular. This will enable casts to be obtained from the mould when it is laid on a flat or purpose-made curved background. No preparation is required either before or between casts and the life of a PVC mould is for as long as is required. Upon the completion of the final cast the PVC may be cut up and reused.

Run case moulding

A run case mould is a flexible reverse mould of even thickness with a shaped back held in position by a plaster case. The advantages of using this type of mould are that the sections of plain mouldings, together with the enrichment, can be kept in line by the shaped back fitting into the run case. Should a curved cast be necessary then the shaped back or case is run to the required radius and the flexible mould fitted into this.

The method used to form a run case from a prepared model is as follows. All moulding grounds must be shellacked and greased and all enrichment well covered by wet newspaper. Do not press the paper into the enrichment as this could form undercut. Cut a wooden template to the shape required for the back of the flexible mould (Figure 12). A mix of class A plaster is then run over the model and paper and its upper surface will present the shape needed for the case. Continue to pass the template along the model until a good shape and smooth surface has been obtained. This 'core' is now treated with shellac and grease and a well reinforced case is cast over the run core and moulding grounds.

When set remove from the model. Remove the core from the case and cut air and funnel holes in the case. The paper is removed from the model and everything should be thoroughly cleaned. The case must be positioned accurately over the model. Where the core was there will now be a void which should be filled with PVC poured through funnels (the funnels are fixed to the case by plaster and canvas wads). The same method is used to hold the case in position. When pouring, start at one end and work along the funnels, allowing the PVC to reach each funnel before pouring. Allow the compound to run freely from the air holes.

Once it has cooled, remove funnels and fixings, turn the case over and remove the PVC from the model. Fit it into the case, making sure all lines are straight, and prepare for casting.

Clay case mould (using PVC)

As mentioned in the section *preparation of models*, clay case work is an ideal method of obtaining PVC reverse moulds from awkwardly shaped ornaments.

Using a truss as an example, the model is fixed to moulding grounds which are then shellacked and greased (Figure 13). Wet paper is placed over the model and part of the moulding grounds (which act as strike off areas). Boards of clay are beaten out, cut to size, and fitted over the paper. With this operation it is important to eliminate areas of undercut with strips of clay. This will ensure that the plaster case when cast will draw away from the clay with ease. Around the perimeter of the clay work a raised lip is formed to act as a continuous joggle.

The back of the clay is smoothed over with paraffin which will also act as a release agent.

A plaster case is now cast over the clay work and moulding grounds, suitably reinforced and levelled off. When the case has set its position is marked out on the moulding grounds for reference then removed for the funnel and air holes to be cut out. The clay and paper are removed and the model checked over and repaired if necessary.

The plaster case is now carefully repositioned and fixed in place; once the funnel is secured the pouring operation can commence as with the run case mould. When the PVC has cooled, the plaster case and PVC mould are removed for preparation before casting can take place.

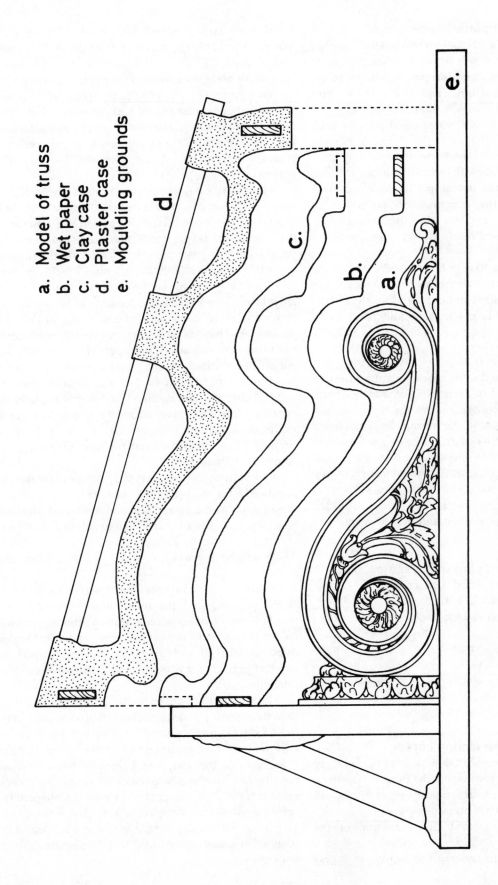

a. Model of truss
b. Wet paper
c. Clay case
d. Plaster case
e. Moulding grounds

Fig.13   Exploded side view of an enriched truss (CLAY CASE)

Casting and fixing plain fibrous work

The reinforcement of a fibrous cast will depend upon the background to which it will be fixed. Where it is to be suspended, the timber reinforcement will be set in the cast in an upright position. This will provide extra rigidity and a means to attach the fixing wires.

Sometimes the carrying timbers wadded to the back of the cast are also used as extra fixing points. Fibrous casts which will be fixed directly to timber ceiling joists or studwork will have the lath in a flat position. The tops of the flat laths are ruled in to a specific thickness. With all the casts made to the same thickness, given that the site timber work is flat and true when the casts are fixed in position, the finished result should be perfectly flat and even.

All plain face casts have a 6 mm by 25 mm rebate along each side or edge. The rebate will be stopped in with hessian scrim soaked in plaster and finished to the existing levels. This reduces the possibilities of cracks on the joints.

Lapped and rebated joints

To form a lapped joint the normal casting rule is fixed in position with a second rule fixed approximately 25 mm back from the casting edge and on the top of it. The casting can be executed in the normal way with extra reinforcement in the rebated area. The finished cast will now have an extra rebate into which a cast of a normal thickness will be fixed. This can be by nailing or screwing the two sections together giving a first class solid joint.

This system is of great benefit when fixing suspended multi-sectional curved, vaulted and domed work.

Stages in casting

1 Prepare model, including sealing and greasing.
2 Cut reinforcement, wood laths, canvas.
3 Gauge plaster, firstings and seconds.
4 Apply firstings, brush and splash.
5 Apply canvas.
6 Apply seconds with brush.
7 Apply wood.
8 Turn in canvas.
9 Brush in and splash.
10 Strike off.

Domework and intersecting curves

The construction of running moulds used for spinning hemispherical domes is basically the same for all sizes. The larger the dome construction the more braces and struts are used. These will help maintain its rigidity and shape when in use against the expansion of the setting plaster.

The working profiles are marked out on the sheet metal using large dividers, compasses or radius rods. Wherever possible the curved outline should be scribed deeply into the metal, which can then be flexed backwards and forwards until it separates. The required curved section will only need to be lightly filed up, and the burred edges cleaned off with an emery cloth. This method requires the minimum of effort and it achieves a first class finish because it eliminates the processes of close cutting with tin-snips and filing down to the profile outlines.

Once the running mould has been constructed, the wood pivot block is cut and fixed securely to the bench. A pivot pin is cut and fixed in the centre and on top of the block. A metal plate with a hole to fit over the pivot pin is fixed to a given point or gig-stick on the running mould. This will enable the running mould to pivot around the pin without any excess and unwanted movement. The sizes of the 'blocks and pins' will vary enormously according to the size of the work being performed. The area to be formed into a dome is cored out using canvas soaked in plaster, draped over lathed plaster ribs or plaster rubble. A false template is fitted to the profile approximately 6–8 mm smaller than the original, and the core is run off to this profile. After the necessary finish has been achieved it is keyed to receive the finish plaster. The false template is removed from the running mould, and the final running off process can commence (Figure 6).

In situations where complete domes cannot be produced, for reasons that include shop facilities, accessibility at the on-site location, transportation and handling, quarter or half sections of the dome are constructed and the required number of casts made. These will be assembled on-site to form the complete dome.

To produce an extra large dome where more than four sections are required, the outline profile can be divided into horizontal sections. Each section of the curve must be 'horsed-up' to be run off in its correct plane. The cast sizes are marked out on the reverse mould and the finished plaster cast is marked with the corresponding reference mark.

Where mouldings are to be fixed to the dome on site their horizontal positions can be etched on to the reverse mould during its formation by means of a small nick, accurately formed on the metal profile.

Sections of the domes and segmental work can be constructed for the sole purpose of running a reverse mould (raised or sunken) to a specific shape. The subsequent casts will therefore be a perfect fit on the actual curved surface. This type of work is normally used when repairing moulded work on existing curved backgrounds.

Vaulting and lunettes

The construction of a reverse mould from which to cast lunettes and intersecting curves can be set out using ribs (plaster templates) cast from a purpose-made mould.

Set out all the outline shapes together with the rib positions. Fix all the ribs temporarily and check them for plumb and alignment before securing them permanently in position. The area in between the ribs can be lathed out and covered with canvas soaked in plaster. A 'floating coat' can now be formed and ruled in with a rebated straight edge, and treated to receive the final plaster coat. The finish coat is ruled in from the top section of the ribs using a straight edge rule, large joint rules and stiff busk. The ribs that form the interesection of the aperture are fixed and finished to the main section. All the bare plaster is now shellacked and the cast sizes are marked out and casting rules fixed. The sections can now be manufactured.

Casting curved and enriched work

Casting circular work, whether it is a flat ceiling centre or large vaulted work, requires more time and attention to the preparation of all reinforcing materials than with 'flat square' casting work. The canvas is cut into manageable sizes called 'laps' (which are strips or squares). These vary according to the shape being cast. The laps help to eliminate large areas of dry canvas bunching up on the 'strike off' sections and aids the turning in sequence when covering the laths. Laps are best used for 'round' work. Full widths of canvas can be used on large curved plain face areas.

The preparation of lath work for curved work is as follows. For flat curved work the laths are cut about three-quarters across the width, and placed in a lath tank to soak, after which they are gently 'bent' at each saw cut until they fit the required shape. To bend a lath flat over a curve the lath is first thoroughly soaked in the lath tank, then it is subjected to a series of light blows with a lath hammer at regular intervals, the lath can now be bent to fit the required curve. All lath work must be covered with canvas and plaster to produce a well integrated cast.

The method of casting is the same as for flat work, with the exception of the firstings being gauged slightly rounder (thicker) than normal. This will counteract the more upright areas, and stop the plaster sliding down to the lower areas. Because of the extra work involved in handling and positioning the canvas laps and laths, the set of the plaster will need to be retarded for a longer period.

Enriched work

When casting deep undercut enriched work the gauged plaster is well sized. It is brushed in the mould. The mould is vibrated by tapping it on the bench to force out most of the trapped air. A second layer of plaster is splashed into the mould to build up its thickness. Deep undercut sections can be reinforced by tucking plaster wads in position in the firstings. The remainder of the casting is as normal. To remove the cast from the mould the reverse mould is eased away from the cast.

In certain situations where delicate enrichments, such as the curled tips of the acanthus leaves used on Corinthian capitals which could get damaged in the removal of the cast from the mould, the actual tips are filled in the reverse mould and the tops are shellacked and greased. The cast can now be made minus the tips of the leaves which are cast separately and fixed to the cast when required. This will avoid possible damage to the reverse mould and solve the casting and removal problems.

New materials for mouldings

Some of the advantages of PVC over gelatine (see Chapter 1) are:

1   It has an almost unlimited life as it can be remelted and reused repeatedly.
2   The preparation work on the models is minimal.
3   It is virtually indestructible as a reverse mould.
4   It is unaffected by the heat and expansion of setting plaster.
5   A PVC reverse mould does not require treatment or release agents prior to casting.
6   Reverse moulds can be stored without being affected by dampness or changes in atmospheric conditions.

Polyvinyl chloride is manufactured in various grades of flexibility to accommodate the complexities of enrichments and styles of ornamentation and the wide range of casting materials. The melting temperatures for each grade must be strictly adhered to and they range from 120 to 170°C.

Although PVC is still the main material used for forming flexible reverse moulding in fibrous plaster-work it has recently been supplemented by another development. Unlike past experiments where hot melt compounds were tried, tested and developed the latest material is 'cold pour'.

The basic constituents are a liquid polysulphide compound, to which a catalyst is added in strict proportions and thoroughly stirred and mixed together before pouring. It is advisable to follow the manufacturer's instructions carefully for the preparation of a model, its pouring and preparation for casting.

Cold pour will form an exact reverse mould down to the smallest details from the original model. However, the main drawback with this material is that it can only be poured *once*. Therefore, great care must be taken when preparing models for pouring. Generally, because of the expense involved, reverse moulds are chosen (whenever possible) that are of a popular design and can be used as stock moulds.

Special grades of both PVC and cold pour materials have been successfully developed to combat the exotherm that is generated when casting with glass fibre.

Glass fibre is another new material which has taken the plastering industry into the chemical age. To produce glass fibre sections in a workshop requires special permission from the local authority. The workshop facilities for glass fibre have to conform to the strict safety regulations, including ventilation and the wearing of safety clothing and protective items. This is because the chemicals used are toxic. The factories are normally located in light industrial areas and away from residential sectors.

At one time expanded polyurethane was used extensively for lightweight props in film studios. It is now banned since one of the dangerous vapours emitted during the pouring process was cyanide.

The materials used with glass fibre casting are various types of polyester resin designed to suit a specific purpose and an organic peroxide catalyst, a selection of glass fibre tissues, cloths and mats, which will form the strength and body of the mould or cast. Always consult the manufacturer's instructions for mixing proportions, the use of sealers and release agents for the models and moulds.

Some advantages of casting in glass fibre are the textures, colouring effects and its weight factor. Special pigments can be used to gain a permanent colouring effect. Also, metal powders can be added to the resin to produce an imitation metal finish and colour. To achieve a finish and texture of sand and cement to represent, for example external mouldings, columns and balusters, dried sand and cement are added to the resin when casting and the finished casts will resemble the required sections. The glass fibre casts are also a fraction of the weight of the traditional methods of forming the external work. A ready mixed GRC is also available.

Another ideal use for glass fibre in fibrous plaster-work is in the manufacture and use of stock reverse moulds, providing the sections of mouldings or enrichment are free of undercut areas. Where necessary the incorporation of an insertion strip of PVC or cold pour of a required enrichment can be used, thereby combining the best qualities of the two materials to form a first class and an extremely durable mould.

The art of the skilled plasterer will hopefully continue to develop and flourish in the area of restoration work. Great care must be taken by employers' organizations and craftsmen alike to preserve and, wherever possible, pass on these precious skills and knowledge to others. These skills and knowledge have already survived many centuries of change and development, and to lose them now would be very short-sighted and a tragic loss to our very rich historical heritage.

6 Repair and restoration of external plastering

Traditionally the terms 'stucco' and 'pargetting' have always been applied to external plasterwork. These terms have already been explained but further reference to them is necessary here. Old pargetting contained no cement as we know it – once again the hardness found on the surface of this work is due largely to the natural maturity of well selected materials and the expert method of handling and tooling. Many efforts have been made over the years to repair this type of work in much the same way as it was when originally applied. Lime and sand, gypsum plaster and sand, and a mixture of all three have all been tried with varying degrees of success. We find it very difficult to accept the idea of using a gypsum plaster externally unless it is either in a very sheltered position or is going to be sealed after hardening. Even then, it only needs a small area of water permeation for the softening up process to start.

For moulded work the process of taking various types of squeezes has already been explored and one of these methods can be used to obtain the necessary reverse moulds. These can then be used for pressing into the applied material. Once again a practice session is highly recommended. Start off by laying the required thickness on the spotboard and pressing the mould into this. At least two points will emerge; does the mould 'draw' cleanly and is the material the correct consistency? (By draw we mean come away cleanly without damaging the cast either through being undercut or having been poorly prepared.) The first point may be put right by gently carving and cleaning to a smooth surface and the

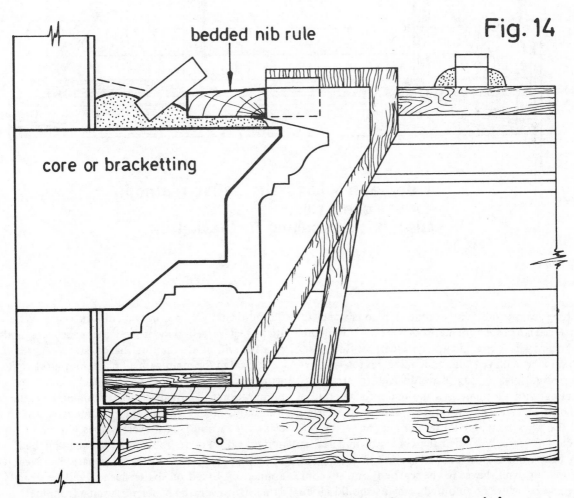

Fig. 14

bedded nib rule

core or bracketting

External opc / sand cornice running mould, nib rule and rabbit

Fig. 15

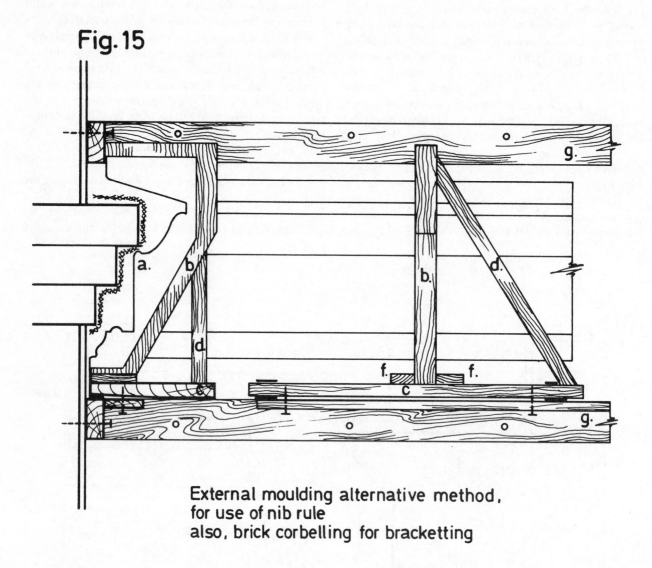

External moulding alternative method, for use of nib rule also, brick corbelling for bracketting

second by sealing and lightly oiling. The consistency of the material is a more difficult problem. To get the depth right one may have to build up a considerable thickness; this cannot be achieved with material that is too soft, yet stiff or round plaster may prove difficult to press.

Dealing with the materials the main consideration could be in all cases of restoration to external plastering – will the work be painted after completion?

If the answer is 'yes' then the choice of material is much wider. Should the answer be 'no' then tests for matching up will have to be carried out. Colour pigments and white or coloured cements should all be seen in a dry state since wet samples will give a different hue. The choice of sand will be important as this too can affect the final appearance in both colour and hardness.

Sand normally comes in two colours, red or yellow, so the effect is self-evident and the sharpness and the grading will affect the final hardness.

To deal in the main with all plaster repairs to external work one must first consider the background and what preparation will be necessary to obtain perfect adhesion. Neat OPC mixed with an external adhesive gives a first class background. However it does eliminate suction and may be very desirable or it may be plain 'bad'. Each operation must be considered separately. Neat OPC applied by brush or spatterdashed will be exactly the same. However, the problems arising from these points are much better than having the work come away after a comparatively short period.

Much of the repair work will commence right at the

top of the building. This may be a short parapet wall with either a coping or a capping moulding or the first feature may be a fairly heavy classical cornice. To deal with moulded work that may have to be run in position seems fairly logical, but the same principles may well apply whether it is a capping moulding, a cornice or a string course. Backings must be checked for soundness and the running mould prepared. In the case of a large cornice, only part of the weathering should be included in the profile and arrangements made for the running to take place on two rules, slipper and nib. With a smaller moulding the full weathering section may be run with or without the help of a nib rule (Figures 14 and 15). In much of the older run external mouldings brick or stone corbelling assisted in forming a type of material and weight-saving bracketing.

Alternatively, metal lathing bracketing may be used. Rods of mild steel are bent to a prescribed shape with additional steel at either end. Holes are drilled into the wall, filled with neat OPC and the rods forced into the holes, spacing for the rods being in the region of 500 mm centres (Figure 16). When the cement has set hard the entire length is wired in metal lathing and rendered with a 1:3 or 4 mix containing hair, sisal or tow. Should the

'bracketing' be brick or stone then this will be spatterdashed and then rendered in a similar mix without the fibrous material.

The larger external mouldings may need several muffle runs. This mean a gradual building out of all members to a good shape. All running in Portland cement and sand is carried out using the wet and dry method. When mixing the materials, half of it should be kept dry; mixed dry and retained. The wet mix may be wetter than one a plasterer would use under normal plastering conditions and it should be applied in a series of thin tight coats. Each coat should be followed by a coat of the dry mix. This is usually flicked on and again, after each coat, the running mould is passed along the full length of the moulding removing all surplus material. The muffle, which is a false or secondary profile, may be moved back several times or just once only. The ideal thickness for obtaining a good finish in OPC/sand is about 5–6 mm, so from this one can see how many runs the job will take. A period of not less than twenty-four hours must elapse between each run and the backing coats must be keyed.

When the final backing coat has been run and the muffle is finally removed for good, the running mould is

Fig.16

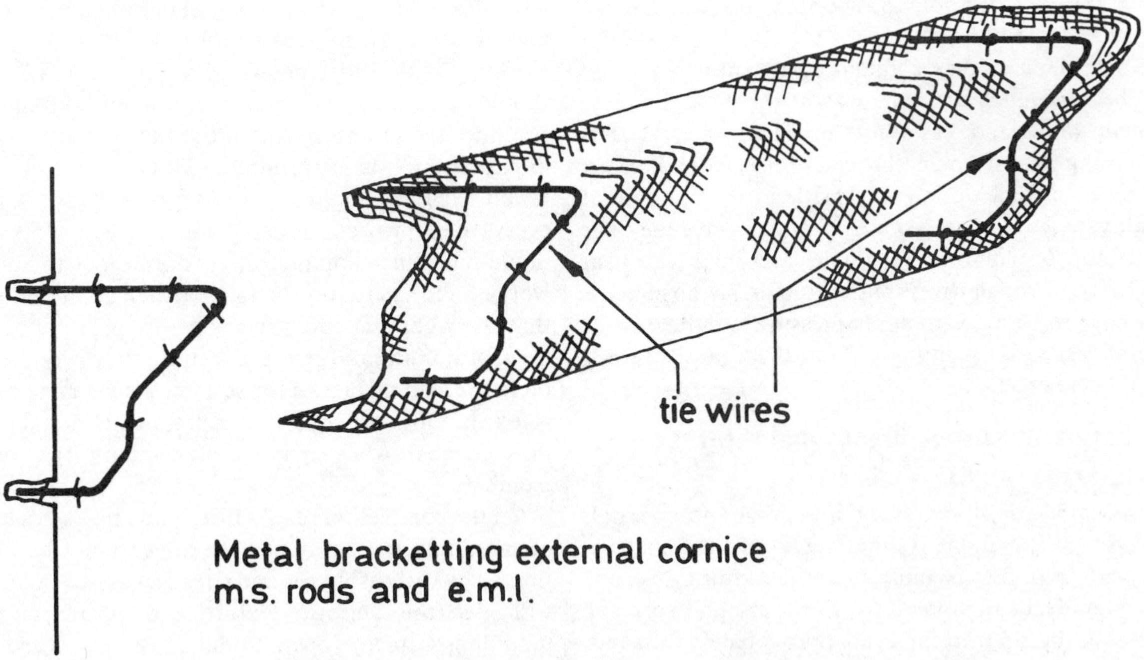

tie wires

Metal bracketting external cornice
m.s. rods and e.m.l.

thoroughly cleaned with all loose particles brushed away from the running rules and the backing. Then both of these are dampened before the final running takes. A fine washed sand will make for a better finish and many plasterers will wash their own sand to get it the way they like it. A fine sieve is one-quarter filled with sand and this is then held under water and gently rotated. The fine grains will fall through the sieve leaving the coarser grains behind. This process is repeated until enough sand has been washed. Half of this may be laid out to dry on a clean plastic sheet. Regular raking will help with the drying out and this can be used to act as 'driers'. The mix for the final coat may depend upon either the written specification or whether the work has to be matched. For the backing coat and muffle run it is usual to add lime when working upon metal lathing. For the backing and muffle coat we would suggest either a 1:1:2½ or a 1:3 mix; some plasterers may prefer to use a liquid plasticizer. Lime putty or a plasticizer should be added to the finish. Again some people will add dry hydrated lime while others will prefer to make it into putty before adding it to the Portland cement and sand mix. As lime putty it generally works more freely but great care is required with the mixing as lumps of unmixed putty will obviously cause trouble when running and to the final job. All mitres, breaks and returns must be worked in while the running progresses. This will ensure a uniform appearance. Once the running is finished and the operation completed then the whole surface of the mouldings should be lightly floated. A good plasterer will have floats of all shapes and sizes to carry out this part of the work. Do not use a sponge as this can damage arrises and spoil lines.

Where the moulding contains ornament it is planted into beds in much the same way as for internal work. Cement and sand casts are prepared, heavy casts containing reinforcement that will project from the back of the casts. Indentations are made in the running at various stages so that they are ready to receive the casts at the appropriate time. The holes are filled with neat OPC and the rod or wire is pushed into it. Arrangements may have to be made to apply pressure to either one or several casts after planting to hold them in position.

Formation of mitres, breaks and returns (using OPC/sand)

It is essential for all mitres, both internal and external, together with small breaks that may occur and that are too small to run, to be built up as the running goes on. Given an ideal situation all the work on a plain cement moulding should then finish at approximately the same time. This will ensure three things: good adhesion; uniform texture; and, as all the work is carried out using the same mix, a uniform colour.

The craftsman will often make his own tools for this particular operation and apart from his normal kit, the main tools will be a set of wooden joint rules and several small, shaped wooden floats. As the running progresses the same amount of attention is paid to the build up of the mitres. On large cornice work many craftsmen will actually produce a set of spare profiles for the muffles and the finish. These are offered up to the mitre or break section just to check that the freehand build up is both sufficient and accurate. Upon the completion of each build up, light keying is necessary.

The operation of finally finishing the mitre, whether internal or external, should follow the same pattern. Commencing from the uppermost member, square in and complete all vertical fillets. To do this internally all one needs to do is to check the projection measurement and when sufficient material has been applied to meet this requirement, hold a large wooden set square on one side of the moulding, and gently use it as a rule till the adjacent side is completed. The first side will have been worked in by rule. Should the mitres be too large for the square then nail the square to a wooden rule, thereby enlarging the square on one side. Proceed downwards in a similar method forming all fillet members, checking either by projection measurements or with the aid of a metal profile. Once all square members are perfect work may commence on the curved members. Build out gently and gradually, then shape, using a wooden joint rule that bares very gently on to the run members. Always keep the joint rule parallel to the members and always work downwards or away from arrises. When working in the fillet members to an external mitre it should be on one side only as it is normally convenient to run one side of an external mitre out with the running mould, using extended running rules and, of course, the rabbit. All that should be necessary is to check and mark every fillet projection mark on the face of the run moulding. When completed, get a colleague to hold the wooden set square on the face of the run moulding so that the right-angled corner is at the projection mark then, by holding and gently working a short wooden rule on to the leading face of the square, the member may be ruled in. Once all square or fillet members have been thus formed work may commence on the curved members.

On the completion of all mitres and breaks in a length of moulding the entire surface area should be lightly floated by various shapes and sizes of wooden float. This will give the uniform texture and ensure that the moulding surface is open. Should it remain closed, as it may well do when well run by metal profile, the appearance will become blotchy at it dries out and after a few years, especially if exposed to severe frost, the smooth surface areas may flake off.

Ashlar and imitation stonemasonry

The most common finish given to external work in ordinary Portland cement and sand is straightforward wood float finish. The name for this is plain face and when this is divided into blocks it is called ashlar. The jointing may be formed in one of three ways: marked by the use of a tool called a jointer; formed by sunken slightly chamfered battens; or run by a double-horsed running mould. Using the first method, a floating coat of $1:\frac{1}{2}:4$ is applied and well keyed by comb scratcher. When this has hardened the finish coat of either $1:\frac{1}{2}:4$ or $1:1:6$ is applied. Then while still green the block lines are struck, a rule is held to the lines and the jointer is pressed into the soft material and drawn along the wall forming a false joint. Matching up to existing work calls for special attention to both background and existing joints, it will also limit the choice of thickness.

When using the sunken batten method, one should apply and key the floating coat, then fix the battens so that the narrowest width is face down on the wall. The slight chamfer will allow the rules to be drawn without causing damage to the arrises. The thickness of the battens will perfectly match the thickness of the plain face, and the width of the battens, the width of the joints. They must be checked for line and when satisfactory can be used as screeds or grounds. A very light oiling of the rules will assist in their removal and one way to do this is to attach part driven in screws into the battens. Withdraw the fixing nails and using the screw heads, pull the rules straight out.

Horizontal run joints can either be run in first, thereby presenting screeds for the blockwork or, alternatively, they can be run in on top of the finished work. Build up the blocks, strike lines for the joints and hold rules in position. Cut as much of the material from the joints as is possible using a smalltool or gauging trowel, then pass a running mould along the rule so that the profile will cut a precision groove or joint in the blockwork. This is, of course, a two or three man job. Vertical joints may be treated in exactly the same way as all mitres and joints which are touched up at the end of the operation.

This method may also be used to form the blocks in preparation for the imitation masonry. There will be two basic differences in this work, however, the first of these being the texture of the blocks. Instead of plain wood float finish, masonry will call for hammered texture, dragged or rolled work and in fact all textures one would normally expect from natural stone. Some

practising may well be necessary before the art of producing a satisfactory finish is attained. The second difference could be in the jointing, plain jointing being replaced with moulded joints and these will have to be run. The methods normally used are as before. Run first to produce grounds for the formation of the blocks or, alternatively, run over the built up block work just before effecting a textured finish.

Materials for all work of this nature will consist of Portland cement, hydrated lime or lime putty and well graded sand. Mixes could well vary from the traditional 1:3 to either $1:\frac{1}{2}:4$ or $1:1:6$. The addition of lime will improve the workability of the material but could affect the final colour. Therefore this must be considered when matching up to old work.

Finally, the repair work to all types of stonework, both real and imitation, may under certain conditions be cast from reverse moulds. Traditionally, the work has always been cast using a good strong OPC/sand mix and the methods of casting are explained later. However, more recently, official approval has been given to cast a new face to very old buildings using GRC (glass fibre reinforced cement), and this can result in the saving of both time and weight. Additional information on this can be obtained from the Blue Circle Company and Pilkington Brothers Limited.

On-site casting using OPC/sand

Unless the required number of all moulded features to be cast from reverse moulds is very high, the operation should be carried out on-site. The features required in classical restoration work will vary from modillions found in cornices, consoles and brackets for supporting pediments, ballusters within a balustrade right down to small enrichment such as triglyphs and egg and dart. Methods for fixing these items require experienced consideration, and it is often better to leave it to the men on-site to decide how to reinforce the casts and whether or not a fixing member should be allowed to project. This follows to a certain extent the principles of the joggle and dowel method of fixing used by stonemasons.

Traditionally, two methods have always been used to obtain casts in Portland cement and sand. Two basic principles must be taken into account when deciding what method of casting should be used. The first concerns the type of reverse mould. Is it to be rigid or flexible? When using a rigid reverse mould of either plaster, GRP or even very rigid PVC, it is safe to use the pressed cement casting method (semi-dry). When using a pliable type of reverse mould one should generally use the normal or wet casting method.

The first method, pressed cement casting based on the principle used on all sandy beaches in summer, consists of mixing the materials, one part OPC, three parts sand, to a semi-dry consistency. In fact the best approach is to mix the two materials thoroughly while still dry, then add water gradually until the required consistency has been obtained. One test for this is to pick up a handful of cement and sand, crush it into one's palm and then release it. If the material stays firm in one piece it is right. If when released it crumbles it is too dry, if water oozes out or it sags then it is too wet. If the reverse mould is either plaster or GRP a very light oiling with clear paraffin is all that is necessary, making sure that the plaster mould has been given the usual three coats of shellac. The rigid PVC mould will require no preparation but may be dusted lightly between casts with French chalk. Reinforcement is not necessary in all casts, but where it is it will vary from mild steel bar to metal lathing or galvanized chicken wire, the latter being used in a similar fashion to canvas in plaster casts.

We are now ready for casting. The mould is prepared, the reinforcing members are ready and the material is mixed. The tools one will need are a gauging trowel, a smalltool and several pieces of timber either dowling or 25 mm by 25 mm batten down to lath. The idea now is to cover the entire surface of the reverse mould with a regular thickness of OPC/sand. The thickness may vary from 25 mm up to, as in the case of a baluster, a solid fill. The material is worked into the mould by hand and by using the wood as a 'rammer'. Now it can be seen why flexible moulds are unsuitable for this task. The mix must be pushed hard into every crevice and one should work systematically so as to ensure that every millimetre gets the same pressure. Once satisfied that everywhere is covered and, if necessary, reinforcing members have been placed, the back of the mould, if not already filled with OPC/sand, may be filled with damp sand up to the level of the strike offs. A flat wooden base should then be placed over the entire area of the cast and the mould and cast turned over on to its back. The mould may now be gently removed, either in one go or, in the case of a piecemould, piece by piece. The cast must now be left on its base board for a period of twenty-four hours, though after a while it may be very lightly sprinkled or sprayed with clean water. On no account must it be allowed to dry out. After twenty-four hours an ideal method of curing is to submerge each cast under water for up to three days. Where this is not possible, then continual sprinkling or spraying must go on for the same length of time. Of course, the longer the curing process is allowed to continue the harder the casts will get, but in general terms three days is considered sufficient for ornamental casts.

The advantage of this method is plain to see. Once the cast has been turned over the mould is free for the production of further casts. In fact it is possible to produce casts very quickly from either one mould or even a battery of moulds. Casting semi-plain modillions, 250 mm by 150 mm by 200 mm deep, on-site many years ago was a task for which one of the authors was allowed fifteen to twenty minutes per cast, or three to four casts for each hour, inclusive of all preparatory work. The texture produced by pressed casting is wonderfully natural, very like real stonework. It has the great advantage too of being completely uniform. It is an operation that can be practised before actual casting commences by using damp sand as the casting medium.

The wet casting method for the production of cement casts is more like the usual method one uses to obtain plaster casts. The material is mixed to a normal workable consistency and a small proportion is made into a rather wetter slurry. In fact many plasterers will either add additional Portland cement or even make up a neat cement mix for this purpose but we do not consider this either entirely necessary or satisfactory. The slurry firsting is then brushed over the face of the prepared reverse mould. Great care must be taken to see that the coating is both complete and uniform in its application. Depending upon the type and size of the cast it may now be necessary to slightly dust the back of the firsting. This is done by mixing OPC and dry sand in the specified proportion and very lightly dusting over the cast with the aid of a hessian bag, too many driers will cause a breakdown in adhesion. More material is now applied and reinforcement added where necessary and the cast is built up either to a solid state or to the normal cast thickness of 25 mm, struck off, cleaned down and left for about twenty-four hours. At the end of this time the cast is removed from the mould and soaked for curing purposes. The reverse mould is then cleaned in readiness for the next cast. The main disadvantage here is obvious: only one cast per day. However there are times when this method is used very satisfactorily. Care is essential when casting otherwise a patchy surface full of airholes may well be the result. Vibrators have been used with both types of casting, sometimes very satisfactorily. However, the main snag in this area is that unless one is careful with the mix the sand tends to fall to the bottom of cast face while the OPC and water comes to the uppermost surface or back of the cast.

GRC in restoration

In recent years the use of GRC (glass reinforced cement) has grown considerably. Many complete stone façades on historical buildings have been replaced by casts in this material. It has several advantages when being used to replace ornamental masonry; it is lighter, it is easy to fix and the bulk of the preparatory work can be done away from the site. Usually GRP (glass reinforced plastic) moulds are prepared for the moulded features and from these moulds GRC casts are obtained. The casts may be as thin as 12–13 mm and no other reinforcement is generally necessary. There appears to be no objection by the authorities to the use of this material as a substitute for the more traditional materials.

Full classical cornices have been cast in this way using a method similar to the wet casting process in OPC. They have been fixed by nailing or screwing through a drilled surface and then made good. At times the cornice has been cast with an additional wall member. This projects some 50 mm down the wall surface. Fixings into the brickwork have been made through this, then the whole of this member has been covered by external cement rendering as specified to match existing. This system was first used many years ago when there was an attempt to introduce a cast glass reinforced plastic cornice in restoration work. In some cases this was fixed by the wall member as before, then the casts were strutted in position and used as shuttering for concrete.

7 Specialist work

Composition

This material was introduced to Britain in the late 1700s and is still used today. Plastic moulding has lessened its usefulness for standard ornament and enrichment but composition is still used in the making of mirror and picture frames and occasionally for fine enrichment on plaster cornices.

A basic recipe for what was once known as a 'London compo' is 8 kg of best quality Scotch glue, 2 litres of linseed oil and 4 kg of ground natural resin. Two containers are necessary and into the first one 3 litres of water are added. The glue is added to the water, dissolved, and stirred continuously. The linsed oil is put into the second pan with the 4 kg of resin. It is heated, dissolved and stirred. When this operation has been completed the contents of the glue pot are added to the pot of resin and thoroughly mixed. Finally, clean whiting is added to bring the compo up to the constituency of a thin dough. It should then be placed on to a clean, dusted board and hand-kneaded.

Originally, the moulds used for composition casting were hand-carved reverse boxwood moulds, sulphur moulds and, at times, even metal moulds. Today, it will probably be hard plaster or GRP. These will all need a light oiling and linseed is as good as any. The warm pliable composition is now cut into strips and laid into the mould. When complete, a damp board is placed over the compo and then placed in a press. Steady even pressure is applied. This will push the composition into every corner of the reverse mould and at the same time cause the compo and damp board to stick together. When the board is lifted from the mould the cast will come with it. All surplus composition is removed by trimming with a sharp knife. This can be re-heated for further use.

To fix the compo, soften the back slightly with steam and when it becomes a little tacky, place in position and pin. Joints must be perfect, thus making stopping unnecessary.

Pargetting

The method of plastering, generally known as pargetting or parge work, was commonplace at one time. It consisted of decorative work carried out in lime and sharp sand. Sometimes the mix contained rye straw to give added tenacity. It has also been found to contain fibrous materials such as sisal, tow and reeds.

While the applied plaster was still plastic, ornament and enrichment was either hand-carved, stamped or rough run. Stamps consisted of reverse moulds of wood, metal or plaster. These were pressed into the pliable plaster rather in the same way as the old butter pats. The plaster was then hand-tooled to a perfect finish. The 'rough run' work consisted of a press mould mounted either on rough wooden wheels or 'skids'. The press mould revolved or was hand-turned and produced stamps in alternate designs. Again the material was hand-tooled with the aid of wooden hand-modelling tools. These preserved the texture for external pargetting while metal tools were generally used for the fatter richer mixes that were used internally.

Plasterers or plaisterers were once called pargettors. Parging at that time basically comprised all plastering in this country. Even today the bricklayer will often use the term 'parge' when referring to the plastering of a chimney flue. In the rough timber-framed houses of several hundred years ago, the plastering was laid to match the rough hard timbers. Very often it would appear that the rough modelling had been carried out by hand trowel. The laying on trowel of that period was more like a present day gauging trowel blade with a laying on trowel handle. They were hand-forged in several sizes and sometimes came to a sharp point, other times the front was rounded. Tools used in modelling resembled the specialist hand-made metal smalltools of today. Corner chisels, spatulas, scratch tools, leaf and squire are just a few examples. Some of these were hand-carved in wood from these shapes many of our wooden modelling tools of today were derived.

Matching up to pargetting can be the most difficult problem. While a good plasterer will cope with the shapes and modelling, it will be the material itself that may cause trouble. Most of the old pargetting was worked in lime plaster, sometimes pure lime/sharp sand, sometimes a mixture of pure and hydraulic lime with, of course, sand. Many aggregates were used including marble dust or chippings and various local aggregates. The lime was naturally slaked and matured and tended to get much harder than today's lime putty. White cement, silver sand and lime have been used to match up to work that is not to be painted but this is not always suitable. Where repairs have been painted, Keene's cement neat or washed sand has been used, but care should be noted as to the degree of exposure. OPC has been permitted in many cases and in general has been successful where colour is of little importance. Several modern materials, basically ready-mixed, have also been used externally but with these thickness may well be the problem. Also it must be remembered that colouring pigments were used in bygone days. Therefore, there is no reason why colours cannot be included in the mixes today. All repair work must be put in the same order as any plastering; the first point being how does one prepare the background? In the case of 300 year old pargetting, the background will probably be wood lathing and we have dealt with this earlier in the book. What is important is when one has to work up to old work edges or even old backing coats. These must be stabilized otherwise breakdown will occur. While not suggesting liquefied cowdung, which in many areas is still considered the best of all traditional methods of controlling suction and stabilizing friable backgrounds, a modern adhesive mixed with OPC and stippled on can do both jobs. However, care must be taken to see that the old work will adhere to this and all loose particles must be lightly brushed away. Again, where large or deep ornament or frieze work is being replaced we suggest applying the new mix in thin coats, even if it means leaving it for some time between coats. Keying to backings and successive coats should be slightly undercut. However, the keying to the final backing should not be too deep as a thin final coat will show these marks, this fault being aptly named 'grinning'.

Hand-carved pargetting will require practice. Fret patterns, chevrons and similar patterns can be formed by using previously prepared wooden templates and thickness rules. Taking a squeeze of external pargetting can be a risky business if the original is unpainted as even clay can stain. Damp paper, clean plastic sheeting and greaseproof paper all have been used under varying conditions. Press the release medium into the ornament and push the clay in hard. After producing a sufficiently large clay squeeze it can now be removed and used as a reverse mould. From this a plaster cast can be obtained and this in turn can be used to produce a good reverse mould for use as either a stamp, press, or even a plain reverse mould. Each step would require attention to perfect the final pressing. Clean up the first plaster cast and again freshen the arrises, etc., within the final mould.

Scagliola

In recent years the word scagliola has come to mean all types of marble produced with the use of plaster. Originally, these marbles were produced by plasterers working *in situ.* Today, they are invariably precast.

The basic material has always been Keene's cement but this is no longer available except when ordered in very large quantities or when made by small independent manufacturers. The plaster is mixed with powdered dyes that will both present the correct colours for the specific type of marble and at the same time be resistant to alkali attack from within the plaster. Water is placed in bowls and the dyes are added to the water, each colour in a separate bowl. Plaster is then added to the coloured water and gauged to a thick consistency, similar to that of a heavy dough. When thoroughly mixed, it may be pushed through a fine sieve so as to ensure it is lump free, the consistency helping to prevent the colours from running.

Casts are produced by laying the coloured plaster to form similar patterns to that of the marble. This may be done in large patterns or small laminations. The mottled effect can be produced by pushing two or more colours through a fine sieve, veining by drawing wires, strings or cottons through the mixes or by laying in, removing and filling the streaks with coloured plaster.

As the mix is relatively stiff, many air holes may be left on the face. These are filled by coloured or white Keene's and rubbed down with fine stones. This process will continue until a perfect surface is acquired, then the cast must be allowed to dry out. Traditionally, when dry, the casts were soaked in a clear oil and polished with paraffin and bees' wax. Today, more up-to-date waxes are frequently used.

The back of the marble casts are usually reinforced by class A plaster and canvas and as the face should not be pierced, all fixing must be from the back in much the same way as real marble cladding is carried out.

8 Faults

The two major faults that occur on antique plasterwork are cracks or cracking, and disintegration. Within the first category there are several types of cracks to look for. Firstly, is the crack constructional? This type of crack will generally have one of two or three means of identification. Is the facework on either side of the crack still in line or does one side project in front of the other? How far inside the plastering can a pencil or screwdriver be inserted before it meets resistence? Finally, how wide is the crack? By applying these tests to the facework before any removal takes place one should know whether the crack is constructional or plaster related only. A projecting surface, a crack depth beyond that of the plaster thickness and a wide opening all suggest something a little more serious than just plaster cracks. Settlement or any movement within the structure will cause one or all of these to happen.

The remedy is to remove all loose plaster on either side of the crack and to see whether or not any repair work to the background is necessary. If the crack is still opening advice should be sought. If not, then clean the crack out and fill it with a good strong backing material. When this has set carry out repairs to the plastering by dovetailing the cracks, filling with class A plaster and sand up to backing coat thickness. Finish with class A gypsum plaster and lime putty 1:2.

Smaller plaster cracks may be dealt with in a similar fashion. Reasonably strong class A mixes will ensure good adhesion provided the cracks are cleaned thoroughly, dampened and, if possible, the edges and back coated with PVA adhesive.

Now to general disintegration; more often than not this is caused either by damp getting in from behind or merely old age. Very often the backing will break up behind the finish and even the mouldings. One good knock and down it will come. This is why care must be taken and the craftsman should be on hand to judge just how much of the moulded work should be saved for squeezes or moulds. If the damp is still penetrating, there may often be telltale patches of efflorescence visible. Water getting into very old lime plaster will cause a general softening up process to occur; then even if it dries out again the backing will not recover its original hardness. All affected work must be removed and the background treated so as to prevent the spread of more water. A good treatment for this is synthaprufe, but it must be remembered that this material, or a similar treatment, will cause the background to become low suction and subsequent coats of plaster should be gauged accordingly.

When the attack by moisture affects the visible surface only, very often the finishing coat of old plastering can be easily brushed off its backing, while the undercoat may well be reasonably sound. A good stabilizer for the undercoat is PVA adhesive brushed well in. Again, it must be remembered that this material will cause either backing or background to become low suction.

Faults to external plastering can fall into the same categories. However, probably the most common fault in old cement and sand work is the breakdown of adhesion between coats. The removal of all loose work should be carried out carefully as heavy hammering will cause other work to loosen on its backing. Decomposition of backgrounds can very often form a major cause of faults in external work. Due to the use of rather strong mixes used on some work, water can get in behind the plasterwork but cannot get out so it will attack the background. When this occurs one of two things will happen. Continual permeation by water will cause the breakdown of adhesion and create a void. At worst, a degree of decomposition will take place. Again the remedy is to neatly and carefully remove all loose work, straighten the edges and treat with an external adhesive. The background should be treated with a spatterdash coat consisting either of OPC/sharp sand 1:2 or neat OPC plus external adhesive. In both cases the mix is stippled on. The thickness of the repair work should be built up in thin coats of around 10–12 mm, well keyed by comb scratcher and left for twenty-four hours. The same method may be used for external ornamental work with clean treated edges and background. Build out gradually to the required thickness and finish to match existing work using wooden floats and wooden joint rules. Never finish with steel tools as these tend to give a surface that is not uniform in texture.

Bibliography

The Art of the Plasterer: George Bankart — Batsford 1908
English Decorative Plasterwork of the Renaissance: M. Jourdain — Batsford 1926
Plastering Plain and Decorative: William Millar — Batsford 1927
Decorative Plasterwork in Great Britain: Lawrence Turner — Country Life 1927
Dublin Decorative Plastering 17th and 18th Centuries: C. P. Curran — Tiranti 1967
Stucco and Decorative Plastering in Europe: Geoffrey Beard — Thames & Hudson 1967
Decorative Plasterwork in Great Britain: Geoffrey Beard — Phaidon 1975
Plastering: A Craftsman's Encyclopaedia: Stagg and Pegg — Collins 1976
Plastering Question and Answer: Stagg and Pegg — Butterworth 1978
Handbook of Building Crafts in Conservation: ed J. Bowyer — Hutchinson 1981
Mortars, Plasters and Renders in Conservation: J. Ashurst — EA & SA 1983
Gypsum Plasters: Department of the Environment Advisory Leaflet No. 2

Appendix A Specification of plastering work

The most important facts when dealing with plastering specifications of all types are as follows:

1 A thorough understanding of the materials in question and what is required of them.
2 The background, its characteristics and the preparation necessary.
3 Material application, thicknesses and the finish.

A good example of this, especially when carrying out restoration work, is the traditionl plasterer's coarse stuff. Three parts clean sharp sand, one part lime with hair or fibrous material added as required were the basic ingredients for many years. The sand was chosen for its cleanliness and quality and the lime was naturally slaked and allowed to mature. Originally, no setting agent was added and this made the material heavily reliant upon suction either supplied by the background or by previous coats of the same material and dry-out time. In this country, up to and including the 1930s, this backing material was used in this condition in many domestic dwellings. A three week 'drying out' period would be allowed between coats, and the result would be high suction backings for all subsequent coats. Very little concrete was found in this type of building but most ceilings would be wood lath and most partitions were of genuine 'breeze'. This of course is not used today but both in themselves were low suction backgrounds.

The finishing coat was always lime setting. This consisted usually of three parts lime putty, two parts fine washed sand. The lime putty was exactly the same material as used to run solid plaster cornices only then it would be mixed with equal proportions of class A gypsum plaster.

Lime putty in those days was made by slaking lump pure lime in purpose-made bins on site. The bin would have been constructed with scaffold boards and its overall size would have been about 4 m by 2 m by 1 m deep and divided into two equal parts. Into one half the lump lime would be deposited and water would be run in by hosepipe until the lime was saturated. It would then erupt violently and give off great heat. Once all this activity had subsided, the milk of lime would be scooped out of its half bin by bucket and poured through a fine sieve into the other half bin. When this operation was completed it would be completely covered by boards and tarpaulin and left for several weeks. The lime would sink to the bottom of the pit and eventually the result would be about three-quarters of the depth lime putty with the upper quarter being water. This water made a perfect seal for the lime putty. As long as it remained the putty would mature naturally and when ready for use would resemble a nice fat rich soft butter or cheese,

really beautiful to use – hence the expression 'spreads like butter'!

More recently lime plastering has given way to the gauged lime plastering, the same basic materials but with OPC added to the coarse stuff and class A, B or C gypsum plaster added to the lime setting. This in turn was followed by the class B gypsum plaster and sand mix and now, of course, we have the premixed era. From this it is correct to assume that modern specification has been made easier to satisfy, but returning to the beginning of this appendix, it is still essential to understand the three points made if one wished to produce the best results.

Today, it is still possible to produce a site-mixed coarse stuff and lime setting stuff, the only basic difference being the use of ready slaked hydrated lime instead of lump lime. The hydrated lime needs to be soaked in water at least overnight to produce lime putty. Many of us still like to have it pushed through a fine sieve before use as this reduces the likelihood of having small knobs of half-soaked lime in the final mix.

For internal plastering where traditional mixes are to be used the following are recommended.

All backgrounds

Backing coarse stuff: 1:3 lime and sand and hair or sisal applied in one coat up to 20 mm thick.

Finish lime setting stuff: 3:2 lime and sand, applied to a well soaked backing, 3 mm thick, applied by trowel, float, trowel method, scoured and polished.

Gauged mixes internal

Backing gauged coarse stuff: 1:1:6 lime, OPC, sand and hair and sisal applied in one coat, up to 20 mm thick.

Finish gauged lime setting 3:2 lime and sand and class A, B or C gypsum plaster as required.

Solid run plaster cornices and mouldings

Backing coats on prepared bracketing class A plaster and coarse stuff 1:2.

Finish class A plaster and putty 1:1.

The hair, sisal or tow used to be added to the mix while it was being gauged. The quantities varied considerably from around 5 kg per m^3 up to as much as 15 kg per m^3. The hair was either ox, goat or horse and had to be well beaten before use. This removed all dust and other impurities and the hair was then distributed into the mortar by an implement known as a hair hook resembling a long handled garden rake with only two curved prongs.

One problem that will frequently arise with restoration work is the building out to match thicknesses occasionally in the region of 75 mm. In this case it is recommended that where raw coarse stuff is being used, it should be applied in two or even three separate coats, each coat being allowed to thoroughly dry out before the next coat is applied. Better still, apply a good dubbing out coat or coats, using OPC gauged coarse stuff and finally leaving only a 20–25 mm thickness to be completed in the traditional lime plasters.

Where the specification allows for the use of modern materials it is essential that the correct grade of undercoat plasters are used on their specified backgrounds. It is possible too that with all of these plasters a good OPC/coarse stuff dubbing out coat may be necessary where the required thickness exceeds those

recommended for the plaster. There are other modern plasters that have been permitted in internal restoration work just as GRC has in external work. Some of these are lime-based while others are resinous. In all cases it is essential to obtain the manufacturer's specification and to see that they are worked to.

External specification will or may bring the additional problem of matching colourwise where the work is not to be painted. Most of the work where OPC was used, that would date from around 1825, would be in a mix that would compare with our 1:3 mix of today. Where matching is not so important, one of today's mixes may well be used, these being 1:1:6 or 1:½:4 (OPC/lime/sand)

Items within the specification that may affect the plasterer are that all timbers used today must be impregnated with approved materials to prevent damp or insect attack. Waterproofing compounds added to internal or external plastering when specified must be of an approved nature and added and/or applied to the manufacturer's instructions.

Appendix B Glossary of plastering terms

Accelerator A material used to accelerate the set of various types of mixes. Basic types include alum for plaster, calcium chloride for OPC/sand mixes and there are several patent materials for use in the same areas.

Additives These are accelerators, colouring agents, hardeners, plasticizers, waterproof compounds, etc. In fact all materials other than aggregates, cements, lime and plasters used in plastering mixes.

Adhesion In plastering, the bond between a wet mix and the background or backing to which it is applied.

Angles Internal and external. These are the intersections of plaster surfaces at varying degrees. Internally are normally hand-formed; externally may be formed or run.

Arris This is the sharp angle formed at the intersection of two surfaces thus forming an external angle. It is also found in a similar position in mouldings.

Ashlar OPC/sand plain face marked out for form blockwork.

Background The surface other than any plastered surface to which plaster is applied, for example brickwork, lath work, blocks, concrete, etc.

Backing This is the plaster undercoat or coats applied to a background; render coat, floating coat or scratch coat.

Binder Traditionally, hair, sisal, tow, etc. Today, the material that causes a mix to harden or set is termed binder.

Bond The adhesion between background and backing and backing and finishing.

Bone To bone means to align several angles, or lines, etc., purely by sighting.

Bracketing and brackets In solid plastering these are a means of saving material in large solid cornice work (Figure 16). To fibrous plastering they mean additional strength in the form of canvas and plaster covered wooden members on the backs of plaster casts, usually across the width.

Break joints and butt and break joints The first indicates that where a lath is broken or jointed in a plaster cast, the break should be reinforced by an additional small piece of lath. A butt and break joint occurs in a traditional wood lath background and indicates a break in the line of lath ends every metre or so. The broken joint should help to eliminate the appearance of long cracks.

Breaks and returns The interruption in the continuity of mouldings and plain surfacing is the break and the return is the continuance of the same work at a different angle.

Carton pierre An old method used to produce fine casts of ornament, it consisted of paper pulp, glue size and whiting mixed to a dough like consistency then pressed into plaster moulds.

Cast, in fibrous plaster A relatively thin coat of plaster 2–3 mm thick, reinforced by wooden members, laths, etc., and hessian canvas; finally, a further thin coat of plaster (firstings and seconds).

Collar A plaster band or bands that will provide the correct outline for a plasterer to use as grounds when forming columns in plaster or OPC mixes.

Core Both in solid and fibrous work this will mean a method of saving both material and labour when producing the final object (See Figures 10, 14 and 15).

Curing The hardening of a material by time in the natural way.

Datum A struck level line from which all setting out can be measured.

Dextrene When made into a solution and added to the water in which plaster is to be mixed will both harden and retard.

Dots Mounds of plaster applied to either background or backing, levelled or plumbed and then used as grounds for the formation of screeds.

Draught Draw, the very slight splay given to all vertical members of a plaster mould. This will enable casts to be removed from the mould without the loss of an arris.

Dressing Bedding, planting, the fixing of lines of enrichment, ornament, etc., to plaster models and mouldings, OPC/sand cornices and cappings.

Driers The dry mix of OPC/sand used to extract surplus water when forming moulded features in this material.

Dubbing out The application of a plastering material to a thickness that exceeds specification requirements. Should normally consist of a 1:3 OPC/sand mix.

Efflorescence A white frothy deposit that appears on the surface of finished work. Due usually to the presence of salt in the background.

Enrichment Lines of enrichment usually consist of lines of bead, bead and reel, dentils, egg and dart, fret, guilloche, honeysuckle, and various leaf designs.

Entasis The convex swell found on classical columns, may be the full height of the column or the upper two thirds.

Expanded metal lath A mild steel expanded wire covered by one coat of bituminous paint.

Feather edge rule A tapered rule used to close in floating and straightening finishing.

Firstings The first coat of casting plaster used when producing fibrous plaster casts.

Floating The undercoat in solid plasterwork that produces a flat, true surface to receive the finishing (setting) coat.

Fresco The painting of freshly applied lime plaster finish so as to produce a combined paint plaster surface.

Gathering on A poor finish produced on run mouldings, caused by either insufficient pressure being applied or by the profile bending.

Gauge Two meanings: to mix; and to measure by means of a gauge rod.

Gelatine A natural moulding compound made from best quality Scotch glue. Melts in a water jacket container and requires much preparation, mainly superseded by PVC.

Gesso A mixture of linseed oil and glue, toughened by the addition of whiting. Used mainly when plasterers formed ornaments by carving in freehand.

Gigstick Radius rod, an arm attached to a running mould and used as a compass leg to run circular features.

GRP Glass reinforced plastic. A resin cast reinforced by fibreglass.

GRC Glass reinforced cement. A ready mixed material of cement and chopped fibre glass used to reproduce traditional external finishes of all types as well as in a more modern method.

Grease plasterers A release agent made up by mixing linseed oil or paraffin and tallow together and applying it to a shellac sealed surface.

Green Freshly applied plaster just before it sets or hardens.

Ground A wooden member used as a screed to work to and a fixing member for the joiner. Also a collar when plastering columns and pilasters. Another use is that of moulding ground in fibrous plaster (see Figure 13).

Hair Used to reinforce solid plaster mixes, goat, oxen or horse hair.

Hessian A woven jute canvas of either 3 or 6 mm mesh, used to reinforce fibrous plaster and the joints in plasterboard ceilings.

Horse Two meanings: firstly, the overal term for a full running mould and secondly, as an alternative to the slipper of a running mould (see Figures 1 and 2).

Insertion mould Basically a reverse plaster mould containing one or more lines of enrichment. This or these are reproduced by having a pliable mould of the complete line in either gelatine or PVC.

Laps Small square or rectangular portions of canvas used to assist the main reinforcing in fibrous plaster casts. They are soaked in plaster and pushed into the back of the cast.

Laths Wooden; types riven and sawn. The riven laths were produced by splitting bulk hardwood into approximately 25 mm wide laths. Sawn laths are cut by machine and are the same width but thickness and length vary considerably to suit requirements.

Lime The term includes all limes used in building with special reference to lime plastering. Here slaked or hydrated fat lime mixed with sand to a ratio of 1:3

produces coarse stuff and mixed with fine washed sand from 2:1 produces lime setting stuff.

Making good   Repair work to new and old plastering.

Mitre   The angle of intersection between two mouldings at any angle other than 180°.

Mitre leaf   A precast plaster leaf used to cover the intersection of a line of enrichment.

Model   The original, either formed by a modeller or by a plasterer using several techniques. From this a mould will be produced.

Moulds reverse   These may be plaster, plaster and flexible plastic, or just flexible plastic obtained from a prepared model. Alternatively, they may be run in plaster using a reverse running mould (Figure 1).

Muffle   A temporary profile used on both solid and reverse running moulds to assist with the build up of the feature. May be of wood, metal or plaster.

Neat   Plaster or cement with no aggregate, no additive, used with nothing added but water.

Pargetting   Solid decorative plastering formed in freehand or by the use of stamp moulds.

Peg mould   A running mould with pegs fixed into the slipper or horse in such a position that they will become the main bearing points (see Figure 7).

Plain face, plaster   Precast fibrous plaster to form areas of plain surfacing on either ceiling or wall.

Plain face OPC/sand   Float finish cement and sand work.

Planting   See *Dressing*.

Plaster, gypsum   The basic gypsum plaster is made from mined or quarried gypsum which is washed, crushed and ground then heated till three-quarters of its water content is driven off. The product is class A gypsum plaster which, when added to clean water, will set within a period of some fifteen to twenty minutes. Various additives and aggregates are added in bulk to produce the classification of gypsum plasters as listed in BS 1191 Parts 1 and 2.

Plaster, resin-based   Modern materials produced for internal and external smooth and textured finishes may be trowel or spray applied. Consist mainly of resin and aggregate and in some instances lime, usually premixed and ready for use.

Plumb   To be perfectly upright.

Polyvinyl acetate   This is the basic material used in the manufacture of bonding agents. When applied they will produce a low suction background.

Polyvinyl chloride   This material is used to produce flexible moulds. It is available in several grades and can be re-heated. The melting point is between 120 and 170°C and a purpose-made appliance is advisable for use in this area. Safety gloves, goggles and mask are also necessary.

Pressed cement casting   A method of casting using OPC and sand, based on the technique used by children building sand castles by casting sand turrets, etc., from damp plastic buckets. The plasterer will normally use plaster moulds to cast balusters, modillions, etc.

Pressed screeds   These are used in the formation of curved backings where run screeds are not suitable. A wooden or plaster template is cut to the curve and pressed into wet plaster laid between accurately placed dots. The curved surface is then ruled to this.

Rabbit, rabbet, rebate   To running moulds a small rule fixed to the underside of the slipper in such a position that it keeps the front edge of the slipper fractionally away from the wall surface (see Figures 14 and 15).

Render coat   Scratch coat, pricking up coat – the first coat used in three coat plastering (i.e. RFS, render, float and set).

Rendering   A term used to cover most external finishes.

Retarder   An additive used to slow down the set of a mix. Glue size will act in this way on gypsum plasters.

Roman cement   A natural cement made from a type of hydraulic clay, brown in colour. Not used today.

Ropes   Canvas cut into lengths, soaked in plaster, squeezed and twisted to form ropes. Usually placed under laths when reinforcing fibrous plaster casts.

Rules Types used by plasterers; rules backed, buried, eccentric, featheredge, nib, notched, running, ruling in, traversing.

Running down This consists of running down short lengths of moulding on either the spot board or a scaffold board, cutting and bedding in position.

Sand The main hand aggregate used in solid plastering. Should always be clean, hard, sharp and gritty.

Scour, scouring The application of a wooden crossgrain and water to a hardening finish coat of lime plaster or class C gypsum plaster. The idea being to retemper and compact the surface which can then be trowelled to a hard polished surface, all surplus fat being trowelled off.

Screed A plaster ground to which other coats of plaster are ruled in.

Seconds The second coat of casting plaster used in casting large fibrous casts. It is always retarded and used to brush in all canvas, soaked laths, laps and ropes.

Selenitic The addition of up to 5 per cent of gypsum plaster to hydraulic lime produces selenitic cement.

Setting Another name for the finishing coat in solid plastering.

Shellac A substance made from lac which is a resinous insect secretion. The shellac flakes are soaked in methylated spirits and the solution used to seal plaster surfaces prior to the application of a release agent.

Sisal A natural material produced from the sisal plant used as a reinforcement and a substitute for hair.

Spatterdash An OPC/sharp sand mix 1:2 prepared to the consistency of a slurry and applied by brush to smooth dense backgrounds to provide a key.

Spinning The running of circular plastering using a gig-stick and pivot.

Stonework Reconstructed; precast, OPC/sand features, produced to look like natural stone usually by including crushed rock as part of the aggregate.

Stopping Filling and finishing gaps in fixed fibrous plasterwork.

Strike offs The edges on the back of a reverse mould used as grounds when 'ruling' off a plaster cast, hence the term striking off.

Stuc (stooc) Gypsum plaster and sand used when forming imitation masonry internally, float finish or mason's drag.

Suction The absorption of water by an applied plaster mix.

Template Used to form angles and other similar features in plaster.

Terrazo A specialist floor laying material consisting of marble chippings and white cement, highly polished.

Throat-drip A sunken member to a horizontal section preventing the spread of water.

Turning As in wood turning, the formation of plaster features by turning on a spindle.

Undercut A section that cannot draw due to the overhang of the ornament.

Wads Canvas dipped in plaster and laid flat over the back of casts, also when joining casts together.

Wax 50 per cent bees' wax and 50 per cent rosin, used as a moulding compound.

Appendix C
Specialist Plasterers

Green & Veronese Ltd,
24 Edison Road,
London N.8

G. Jackson & Sons,
Rathbone Works,
Rainville Road
London W.6

Openwood,
Acell House,
Stockley Close,
Stockley Road,
West Drayton,
Middlesex.

D. C. Pinn,
8 Bowden Street,
Kennington
London S.E.11

Thomas & Wilson,
454 Fulham Road,
London S.W.6

Specialist Suppliers

Blue Circle Group,
Therapia Lane,
off Beddington Lane,
Croydon CR9 4EY

British Gypsum Ltd,
Westfield,
360 Singlewell Road,
Gravesend,
Kent DA11 7RZ

Laths:
Jewsons,
Carnwath Road,
London S.W.6

Hair:
J. Milton & Co.,
12 Vernay Road,
London S.E.16

Mortars:
Tilcon Ltd.,
Mortar & Special Products Division,
Lingerfield Scotton,
Knaresborough,
North Yorkshire HG5 9JN

RMC Mortars Ltd.,
Holly House,
74 Holly Walk,
Royal Leamington Spa,
Warwickshire CV32 4JD

General:
A. Randall Ltd.,
Supremacy House,
Hurstwood Road,
Golders Green,
London.